SARAH FARRELL WITH ANDREW JENNINGS
TIMES TABLES
NINJA

BLOOMSBURY EDUCATION

LONDON OXFORD NEW YORK NEW DELHI SYDNEY

BLOOMSBURY EDUCATION
Bloomsbury Publishing Plc
50 Bedford Square, London, WC1B 3DP, UK
29 Earlsfort Terrace, Dublin 2, Ireland

BLOOMSBURY, BLOOMSBURY EDUCATION and the Diana logo are trademarks of
Bloomsbury Publishing Plc

First published in Great Britain, 2022
This edition published in Great Britain, 2022

A catalogue record for this book is available from the British Library

ISBN: PB: 978-1-8019-9040-0; ePDF: 978-1-8019-9039-4

2 4 6 8 10 9 7 5 3 1

Text design by Marcus Duck Design

Printed and bound in the UK by CPI Group Ltd, CR0 4YY

MIX
Paper from
responsible sources
FSC® C013604

To find out more about our authors and books visit www.bloomsbury.com and sign up
for our newsletters

CONTENTS

OTHER NINJA RESOURCES FOR TEACHERS

ARITHMETIC NINJA
ANDREW JENNINGS WITH SARAH FARRELL AND PAUL TUCKER

The *Arithmetic Ninja* series is the perfect resource for any primary classroom. Ideal for daily maths practice and quick lesson starters, each photocopiable book includes 10 questions per day and 39 bonus weekly ninja challenges – 702 question cards in total. Covering a range of key topics in the primary National Curriculum for Mathematics, these flexible resources will ensure all pupils are fully-fledged arithmetic ninjas by the end of the year.

ALSO BY ANDREW JENNINGS

VOCABULARY NINJA

A practical guide featuring strategies and photocopiable activities to help transform pupils into vocabulary ninjas. With easy-to-follow theory and teaching approaches, as well as key curriculum topic vocabulary, etymology and phrases, this book will help bring the primary curriculum to life.

COMPREHENSION NINJA NON-FICTION

A set of six books for ages 5–11 that provide strategies and carefully curated resources to teach the key comprehension skills of skimming, scanning and retrieving information effectively. Each book presents 24 high-quality non-fiction texts and photocopiable activities with strong links to the National Curriculum.

FOR CHILDREN

WRITE LIKE A NINJA

A pocket-sized book packed full of all the grammar, vocabulary and sentence structures that children need in order to improve and develop their writing skills. Fully aligned to the Key Stage 2 National Curriculum, this book is designed to be used independently by pupils both in the classroom and at home.

BE A MATHS NINJA

Be a Maths Ninja is jam-packed with key concepts, mathematical vocabulary and practice advice to support every child's growing independence in maths. It covers all the key areas of the National Curriculum for Key Stage 2 and is perfect for children needing all the important maths facts at their fingertips.

FURTHER RESOURCES FOR SCHOOLS, TEACHERS AND CHILDREN ONLINE

Head to www.vocabularyninja.co.uk and follow @VocabularyNinja on Twitter for more teaching and learning resources to support the teaching of vocabulary, reading, writing and the wider primary curriculum.

INTRODUCTION

Times tables knowledge underpins almost every concept in the maths curriculum. With a strong understanding of the multiplication and division facts in the times tables to 12, pupils will be in a much better position to tackle concepts such as equivalent fractions and long multiplication. *Times Tables Ninja* has been designed to be an essential resource for building and developing understanding of the times tables and how they relate to the maths objectives set out by the National Curriculum.

Introducing pupils to times tables

The most important element of learning multiplication facts is to know that they are commutative (a x b = b x a). Pupils should be exposed to various different concrete, pictorial and abstract representations to build the understanding of this concept and be able to then apply it to other mathematical concepts. To start with, multiplication facts should be introduced through concrete manipulatives, such as counters, to form arrays. For example, the multiplication fact 2 x 3 = 6 could be represented by two rows of three counters or three rows of two counters. Appropriate vocabulary at this point could be 'two lots of three is equal to six', or 'six is equal to three lots of two'.

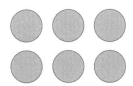

After the concrete representations, the multiplication facts can be explored through pictorial methods. This could begin with a non-concrete visual of an array, before moving on to part-whole models. These help to build the understanding that the multiplication facts are commutative, so 2 x 3 = 3 x 2.

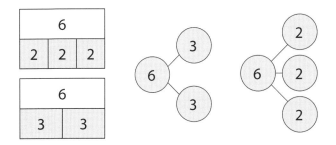

After this, the multiplication fact can be discussed in more abstract terms, e.g. 2 x 3 = 6. This fact can then be extrapolated to include place value knowledge, such as 20 x 3 = 60 or 200 x 3 = 600. It is also important that pupils become used to seeing the facts represented in different ways. For example:

• 2 x 3 = 6

• 3 x 2 = 6

• 6 = 2 x 3

• 6 = 3 x 2

• 6 ÷ 3 = 2

• 6 ÷ 2 = 3

• 2 = 6 ÷ 3

• 3 = 6 ÷ 2

How to use the book

This book contains a chapter on each of the times tables from 2 to 12 and then a chapter covering mixed multiplication facts from all the tables. Each chapter focuses on fluency and rapid recall in the multiplication and division facts, before moving onto applying that knowledge to other areas of maths, such as shape, scale factors and fractions, which enables pupils to see how the multiplication facts relate to the big concepts that they are learning. This is a versatile resource: it could be used in maths lessons as a worksheet, as part of homework to learn times tables or as a small-group times-table-focused intervention.

There are two certificates included in the book which you can use to celebrate times table achievements. The certificate on page 151 can be filled in with a child's name after each times table chapter has been completed. The certificate on page 152 can be used on completion of the book to certify that the child has mastered every table and is now officially a Times Tables Ninja!

Vocabulary to use with times tables

Array: An array is a visual representation of multiplication and division. It is shown using columns and rows.

Digit: Digits are used to form numerals. There are only ten digits (0, 1, 2, 3, 4, 5, 6, 7, 8, 9). The numeral 456 is made up of the digits 4, 5 and 6.

Factor: A factor is a number that divides into another number without leaving a remainder. For example, 5 is a factor of 25 because 25 can be divided by 5 exactly.

Lots of/Groups of/Sets of: Children will often be introduced to multiplication and division using this vocabulary before using the multiplication and division symbols, e.g. 12 is equal to 3 lots of 4, or 4 groups of 3 is equal to 12.

Multiple: A multiple is a number that is found in the times table of another number, e.g. 12 is a multiple of 3.

Product: The product is the result of multiplying two or more number together. For example, the product of 5 and 3 is 15.

Repeated addition: Repeated addition is a way of showing multiplication, e.g. $3 \times 4 = 3 + 3 + 3 + 3$.

Repeated subtraction: Repeated subtraction is a way of showing division, e.g. $12 \div 4$ can be found by subtracting 4 from 12 until there is no remainder. In this example, it can be subtracted three times.

Times table hints

1 times table

Multiplying any number by 1 does not change it, e.g. $5 \times 1 = 5$.

2 times table

Multiplying a number by two doubles it, e.g. $5 \times 2 = 10$; double 5 is equal to 10.

3 times table

The digits of numbers in the 3 times table add up to multiples of 3. In the number 24, the digits 2 and 4 add up to 6, which is a multiple of 3.

4 times table

The 4 times table is double the 2 times table, e.g. $3 \times 2 = 6$ and $3 \times 4 = 12$.

5 times table

All multiples of 5 end in either a 5 or a 0. If an odd number is multiplied by 5, the product will end in 5. If an even number is multiplied by 5, the product will end in 0.

6 times table

The 6 times table is double the 3 times table, e.g. $4 \times 3 = 12$ and $8 \times 3 = 24$.

7 times table

Numbers in the 7 times table can be found by combining numbers in the 5 times table and in the 2 times table.

$7 \times 8 = 56 \longrightarrow 5 \times 8 = 40$ and $2 \times 8 = 16$. The sum of 40 and 16 is 56.

$7 \times 9 = 63 \longrightarrow 5 \times 9 = 45$ and $2 \times 9 = 18$. The sum of 45 and 18 is 63.

8 times table

The 8 times table is double the 4 times table, e.g. $3 \times 4 = 12$ and $3 \times 8 = 24$.

Adding 8 to a number mentally can be done more easily by adding 10 and then subtracting 2.

9 times table

The digits in all multiples of 9 add up to 9:

$5 \times 9 = 45$ $4 + 5 = 9$

10 times table

All multiples of 10 end in 0.

11 times table

All the multiples of 11 less than one hundred have the same tens digit and ones digit:

$5 \times 11 = 55$ $6 \times 11 = 66$

12 times table

Numbers in the 12 times table can be found by combining numbers in the 10 times table and in the 2 times table:

$12 \times 7 = 84 \longrightarrow 10 \times 7 = 70$ and $2 \times 7 = 14$. The sum of 70 and 14 is 84.

$12 \times 9 = 108 \longrightarrow 10 \times 9 = 90$ and $2 \times 9 = 18$. The sum of 90 and 18 is 108.

Adding 12 to a number mentally can be done more easily by adding 10 and then adding 2.

2 TIMES TABLE

Can you see any patterns in the 2 times table?

1 **Shade in or circle the multiples of 2 up to 100.**

1	2	3	4	5	6	7	8	9	10
11	12	13	14	15	16	17	18	19	20
21	22	23	24	25	26	27	28	29	30
31	32	33	34	35	36	37	38	39	40
41	42	43	44	45	46	47	48	49	50
51	52	53	54	55	56	57	58	59	60
61	62	63	64	65	66	67	68	69	70
71	72	73	74	75	76	77	78	79	80
81	82	83	84	85	86	87	88	89	90
91	92	93	94	95	96	97	98	99	100

2 **Find and circle the 2 times table in this number search.**

2	x	2	=	4	2	5	x	2	=	10	16	3
12	13	x	2	x	3	10	9	2	x	2	x	9
10	x	2	4	2	=	4	x	x	3	=	2	3
x	14	=	2	=	8	x	2	4	x	20	=	x
2	x	2	=	8	x	2	=	16	2	22	8	2
=	6	4	6	16	6	12	18	x	=	14	6	=
20	11	x	4	x	2	x	6	=	7	22	24	6
6	1	x	2	=	2	6	2	11	x	=	7	x
8	x	2	=	20	4	=	2	=	8	2	x	2
12	x	2	=	24	18	x	12	3	9	x	6	16
10	x	2	7	x	2	=	14	x	=	11	24	2

2 TIMES TABLE

Fill in the missing numbers.

Set 1

3	x	2	=	
	x	2	=	12
	x	2	=	14
	x	2	=	20
2	÷	2	=	
	÷	2	=	5
11	x	2	=	
12	x	2	=	
	÷	2	=	6
14	÷	2	=	

Set 2

	÷	2	=	4
	x	2	=	8
5	x	2	=	
8	x	2	=	
	x	2	=	18
	÷	2	=	8
18	÷	2	=	
	÷	2	=	10
22	÷	2	=	
24	÷	2	=	

Set 3

	x	2	=	18
16	÷	2	=	
18	÷	2	=	
	÷	2	=	10
	÷	2	=	11
24	÷	2	=	
	÷	2	=	2
	÷	2	=	3
1	x	2	=	
2	x	2	=	

Set 4

4	÷	2	=	
	÷	2	=	3
1	x	2	=	
10	x	2	=	
	÷	2	=	1
	x	2	=	4
16	÷	2	=	
18	÷	2	=	
	÷	2	=	10
10	÷	2	=	

Set 5

11	x	2	=	
12	x	2	=	
	÷	2	=	6
	÷	2	=	11
	÷	2	=	12
3	x	2	=	
6	x	2	=	
	x	2	=	14
14	÷	2	=	
8	÷	2	=	

Set 6

	÷	2	=	8
18	÷	2	=	
	÷	2	=	10
10	÷	2	=	
	=	4	÷	2
3	=		÷	2
	=	8	÷	2
24	÷	2	=	
	x	2	=	6
6	x	2	=	

Set 7

	÷	2	=	11
16	=		x	2
	=	9	x	2
	=	10	x	2
22	=		x	2
4	x	2	=	
	=	4	x	2
10	=		x	2
	=	6	x	2
14	=		x	2

Set 8

	=	16	÷	2
9	=		÷	2
10	=		÷	2
11	=		÷	2
	x	2	=	22
24	=		x	2
	x	2	=	10
8	x	2	=	
	x	2	=	18
2	=		x	2

Set 9

	=	2	x	2
6	=		x	2
1	=		÷	2
7	x		=	14
	÷	2	=	7
	=	10	÷	2
	=	12	÷	2
7	=		÷	2
	÷	2	=	4
12	=		÷	2

1 Complete the maze by drawing a line through multiples of 2. Watch out for dead ends!

START HERE

2	1	5	7	23	15	17	24	26	27	25	24	21
8	9	8	7	13	12	19	21	22	24	23	21	28
6	10	12	21	23	5	7	1	2	7	3	6	8
1	3	20	6	11	16	13	21	9	19	15	22	12
17	15	22	25	23	1	7	11	24	1	3	17	10
19	12	24	15	17	19	21	14	18	24	22	18	23
13	11	2	16	18	5	7	12	21	13	3	14	3
15	18	21	11	14	12	8	10	17	1	2	12	5
12	22	25	15	17	21	22	17	19	5	22	16	13
17	4	5	7	19	13	10	16	17	21	23	2	15
2	6	12	13	4	17	23	19	8	1	5	4	**EXIT**

2 Fill in the gaps in the table.

a	2 + 2 + 2 + 2 + 2 + 2	6 x 2	12
b		1 x 2	2
c	2 + 2 + 2 + 2 + 2	5 x 2	
d	2 + 2		4
e		11 x 2	22
f	2 + 2 + 2 + 2 + 2 + 2 + 2 + 2		16
g	2 + 2 + 2 + 2	4 x 2	
h	2 + 2 + 2 + 2 + 2 + 2 + 2 + 2 + 2 + 2 + 2 + 2	12 x 2	
i		10 x 2	20
j	2 + 2 + 2		6
k	2 + 2 + 2 + 2 + 2 + 2 + 2 + 2 + 2	9 x 2	
l	2 + 2 + 2 + 2 + 2 + 2 + 2		14

1 Calculate the area of each of these rectangles (not drawn to scale).

Example

12 cm

24 cm²

2 cm   12 cm x 2 cm = 24 cm²

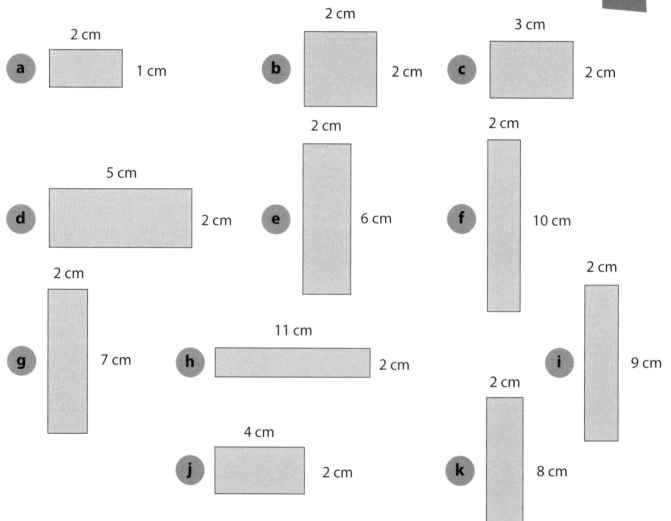

a 2 cm / 1 cm

b 2 cm / 2 cm

c 3 cm / 2 cm

d 5 cm / 2 cm

e 2 cm / 6 cm

f 2 cm / 10 cm

g 2 cm / 7 cm

h 11 cm / 2 cm

i 2 cm / 9 cm

j 4 cm / 2 cm

k 2 cm / 8 cm

2 Find the area of rectangles with these measurements.

Ninja Challenge

a	50 cm long and 2 cm wide	
b	2 cm long and 300 cm wide	
c	2 cm long and 20 cm wide	

1 Use the known multiplication facts to answer these questions.

Example		
1 x 2 =	2	
10 x 2 =	20	
100 x 2 =	200	

a	2 x 2 =	
	20 x 2 =	
	200 x 2 =	

b	3 x 2 =	
	30 x 2 =	
	300 x 2 =	

c	4 x 2 =	
	40 x 2 =	
	400 x 2 =	

d	5 x 2 =	
	50 x 2 =	
	500 x 2 =	

e	6 x 2 =	
	60 x 2 =	
	600 x 2 =	

f	7 x 2 =	
	70 x 2 =	
	700 x 2 =	

g	8 x 2 =	
	80 x 2 =	
	800 x 2 =	

h	9 x 2 =	
	90 x 2 =	
	900 x 2 =	

i	10 x 2 =	
	100 x 2 =	
	1,000 x 2 =	

j	11 x 2 =	
	110 x 2 =	
	1,100 x 2 =	

k	12 x 2 =	
	120 x 2 =	
	1,200 x 2 =	

2 Use the known multiplication facts to answer these questions.

Example	36 x 2	
30 x 2	60	
6 x 2	12	
Total:	72	

a	28 x 2	
20 x 2		
8 x 2		
Total:		

b	75 x 2	
70 x 2		
5 x 2		
Total:		

c	39 x 2	
30 x 2		
9 x 2		
Total:		

d	57 x 2	
50 x 2		
7 x 2		
Total:		

e	48 x 2	
40 x 2		
8 x 2		
Total:		

f	284 x 2	
200 x 2		
80 x 2		
4 x 2		
Total:		

g	472 x 2	
400 x 2		
70 x 2		
2 x 2		
Total:		

h	395 x 2	
300 x 2		
90 x 2		
5 x 2		
Total:		

6

Complete these short division questions using the 2 times table.

$732 \div 2 = 366$

```
        3    6    6
   2  |  7  ¹3  ¹2
```

You could write out the times table to help you with these questions.

1
```
2 |  3   2   2
```

2
```
2 |  2   6   2
```

3
```
2 |  4   6   2
```

4
```
2 |  1   2   4
```

5
```
2 |  3   2   8
```

6
```
2 |  8   6   0
```

7
```
2 |  7   3   8
```

8
```
2 |  2   1   4
```

9
```
2 |  2   3   2
```

10	672	÷	2	=
11	422	÷	2	=
12	366	÷	2	=
13	2,232	÷	2	=

14	3,464	÷	2	=
15	1,642	÷	2	=
16	2,632	÷	2	=
17	6,766	÷	2	=

Calculations

Use this space for jottings and written calculations.

Write the multiplication or division calculation and answer for each of these word problems.

1	1 cat has 2 ears. How many ears do 8 cats have?	
2	A teacher shares 12 pencils out between 2 children. How many will they receive each?	
3	2 children have 11 sweets each. How many do they have altogether?	
4	A man has 6 pairs of shoes. How many shoes does he have in total?	
5	Some children line up in pairs. There are 12 pairs. How many children are there altogether?	
6	Drinks come in packs of 2. How many packs will be needed for 8 children?	
7	There are 6 pieces of wood in a pile. A child paints 2 circles on each piece of wood. How many circles are painted?	
8	There are 10 pairs of wellies on the shoe rack. How many wellies are there in total?	
9	2 children share £6 equally between themselves. How much will they get each?	
10	A pair of children split 120 marbles equally between themselves. How many marbles will they receive each?	
11	A necklace is on sale for half price. If it cost £80 originally, how much will it cost now?	
12	A man sells two games for £30 each. How much money will he get in total?	
13	2 children each get 25 points in a game. How many points do they have in total?	
14	A man has 16 apples. He cuts them all in half. How many apple halves does he have?	

Use the 2 times table to find these equivalent fractions.

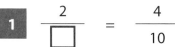

Example

$$\frac{2}{10} = \frac{1}{5} \qquad \frac{3}{5} = \frac{6}{10}$$

÷ 2 ... x 2 ... ÷ 2 ... x 2

Multiply or divide the numerator and the denominator by the same number.

1 $\dfrac{2}{\square} = \dfrac{4}{10}$

2 $\dfrac{14}{18} = \dfrac{\square}{9}$

3 $\dfrac{2}{7} = \dfrac{\square}{14}$

4 $\dfrac{22}{24} = \dfrac{11}{\square}$

5 $\dfrac{10}{\square} = \dfrac{5}{8}$

6 $\dfrac{\square}{14} = \dfrac{6}{7}$

7 $\dfrac{6}{22} = \dfrac{\square}{11}$

8 $\dfrac{10}{20} = \dfrac{20}{\square}$

9 $\dfrac{8}{11} = \dfrac{\square}{22}$

10 $\dfrac{6}{\square} = \dfrac{3}{20}$

11 $\dfrac{\square}{66} = \dfrac{10}{33}$

12 $\dfrac{3}{15} = \dfrac{6}{\square}$

13 $\dfrac{2}{11} = \dfrac{\square}{22}$

14 $\dfrac{14}{16} = \dfrac{7}{\square}$

15 $\dfrac{8}{24} = \dfrac{\square}{12}$

16 $\dfrac{15}{16} = \dfrac{30}{\square}$

17 $\dfrac{24}{30} = \dfrac{\square}{60}$

18 $\dfrac{10}{12} = \dfrac{20}{\square}$

19 $\dfrac{2}{11} = \dfrac{\square}{22}$

20 $\dfrac{18}{30} = \dfrac{\square}{15}$

21 $\dfrac{50}{60} = \dfrac{25}{\square}$

22 $\dfrac{4}{6} = \dfrac{\square}{12}$

Use the given fraction to find the whole number.

Example

$\frac{1}{2}$ of 14 is 7

7	7
14	

1 $\frac{1}{2}$ of ☐ is 8

8	

2 $\frac{1}{2}$ of ☐ is 5

5	

3 $\frac{1}{2}$ of ☐ is 4

4	

4 $\frac{1}{2}$ of ☐ is 3

3	

5 $\frac{1}{2}$ of ☐ is 2

2	

6 $\frac{1}{2}$ of ☐ is 11

11	

7 $\frac{1}{2}$ of ☐ is 10

10	

8 $\frac{1}{2}$ of ☐ is 6

6	

9 $\frac{1}{2}$ of ☐ is 12

10 $\frac{1}{2}$ of ☐ is 9

11 $\frac{1}{2}$ of ☐ is 13

12 $\frac{1}{2}$ of ☐ is 20

13 $\frac{1}{2}$ of ☐ is 50

14 $\frac{1}{2}$ of ☐ is 25

15 $\frac{1}{2}$ of ☐ is 60

16 $\frac{1}{2}$ of ☐ is 45

17 $\frac{1}{2}$ of ☐ is 23

18 $\frac{1}{2}$ of ☐ is 400

Find $\frac{1}{2}$ of the numbers below by dividing them by 2.

Example

$\frac{1}{2}$ of 10 = 5

5	5
10	

1 $\frac{1}{2}$ of 20 =

2 $\frac{1}{2}$ of 2 =

3 $\frac{1}{2}$ of 16 =

4 $\frac{1}{2}$ of 4 =

5 $\frac{1}{2}$ of 8 =

6 $\frac{1}{2}$ of 22 =

7 $\frac{1}{2}$ of 18 =

8 $\frac{1}{2}$ of 6 =

9 $\frac{1}{2}$ of 24 =

10 $\frac{1}{2}$ of 14 =

11 $\frac{1}{2}$ of 12 =

12 $\frac{1}{2}$ of 26 =

13 $\frac{1}{2}$ of 200 =

14 $\frac{1}{2}$ of 240 =

15 $\frac{1}{2}$ of 80 =

16 $\frac{1}{2}$ of 32 =

17 $\frac{1}{2}$ of 48 =

18 $\frac{1}{2}$ of 600 =

Adjust these ingredients lists by the amounts shown. Use the number facts if you need to.

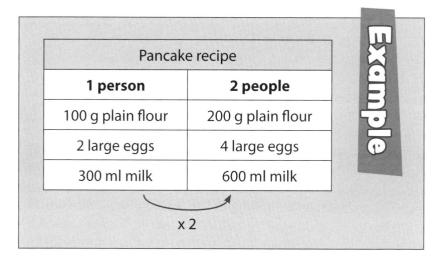

Example

Pancake recipe	
1 person	**2 people**
100 g plain flour	200 g plain flour
2 large eggs	4 large eggs
300 ml milk	600 ml milk

x 2

Multiply or divide each ingredient by the same number to scale the recipe up or down.

1

Milkshake recipe	
2 people	**4 people**
200 ml milk	
3 bananas	
2 chocolate bars	

x 2

2

Flapjack recipe	
1 flapjack traybake	**2 flapjack traybakes**
200 g oats	
120 g butter	
110 g brown sugar	

x 2

3

Fudge recipe	
40 pieces	**20 pieces**
400 g sugar	
300 ml cream	
50 g butter	

÷ 2

4

Rock cakes recipe	
16 rock cakes	**8 rock cakes**
220 g flour	
80 g sugar	
120 g butter	
160 g dried fruit	

÷ 2

5

Smoothie recipe	
1 smoothie	**2 smoothies**
11 strawberries	
9 cherries	
50 ml yoghurt	
100 ml juice	

x 2

Calculations

Use this space for jottings and written calculations.

12

Find the perimeters of these regular polygons (not drawn to scale).

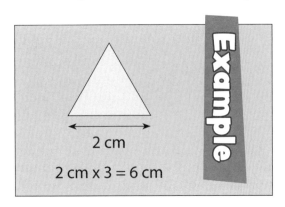

Example

2 cm

2 cm x 3 = 6 cm

Multiply the length of one side by the number of sides to find the perimeter of regular polygons.

1

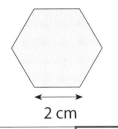

2 cm

Answer:

2

2 cm

Answer:

3

2 cm

Answer:

4

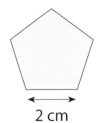

2 cm

Answer:

5

2 cm

Answer:

6

2 cm

Answer:

7

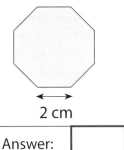

2 cm

Answer:

8

20 cm

Answer:

9

20 cm

Answer:

10

20 cm

Answer:

11

20 cm

Answer:

12

20 cm

Answer:

Can you see any patterns in the 3 times table?

1 **Shade in or circle the multiples of 3 up to 100.**

1	2	3	4	5	6	7	8	9	10
11	12	13	14	15	16	17	18	19	20
21	22	23	24	25	26	27	28	29	30
31	32	33	34	35	36	37	38	39	40
41	42	43	44	45	46	47	48	49	50
51	52	53	54	55	56	57	58	59	60
61	62	63	64	65	66	67	68	69	70
71	72	73	74	75	76	77	78	79	80
81	82	83	84	85	86	87	88	89	90
91	92	93	94	95	96	97	98	99	100

2 **Find and circle the 3 times table in this number search.**

1	x	3	=	3	6	7	8	x	3	=	24	6
4	x	3	=	16	x	x	x	11	x	3	3	9
11	x	3	=	36	24	3	3	3	9	12	x	x
9	5	x	3	10	x	3	=	30	=	15	3	3
11	x	3	=	33	18	36	4	9	8	14	=	=
12	12	3	x	5	x	4	18	x	8	2	6	27
2	9	x	4	x	3	=	12	3	7	x	3	7
x	9	12	3	3	3	x	3	=	x	3	3	x
3	36	x	9	=	24	27	33	30	3	=	18	=
=	33	8	3	15	36	6	x	3	=	18	27	24
6	12	x	3	=	4	x	3	=	21	30	33	3

3 TIMES TABLE

Fill in the missing numbers.

Set 1				
7	x	3	=	
	=	6	x	3
	=	7	x	3
	÷	3	=	2
12	=		x	3
	=	5	x	3
6	x	3	=	
27	÷	3	=	
	÷	3	=	10
33	÷	3	=	

Set 2				
36	÷	3	=	
	÷	3	=	3
2	=		÷	3
	=	9	÷	3
4	=		÷	3
5	=		÷	3
	=	18	÷	3
	=	21	÷	3
8	=		÷	3
10	x	3	=	

Set 3				
	x	3	=	33
	=	10	x	3
33	=		x	3
	x	3	=	6
3	x	3	=	
	x	3	=	36
	=	1	x	3
6	=		x	3
	=	27	÷	3
10	=		÷	3

Set 4				
	x	3	=	6
3	x	3	=	
	x	3	=	27
	÷	3	=	3
1	x	3	=	
	=	33	÷	3
12	=		÷	3
	÷	3	=	4
	÷	3	=	5
18	÷	3	=	

Set 5				
24	=		x	3
	=	9	x	3
9	=		x	3
	x	3	=	36
3	=		x	3
6	=		x	3
	=	27	÷	3
10	=		÷	3
	x	3	=	12
5	x	3	=	

Set 6				
5	x	3	=	
	x	3	=	24
36	=		x	3
	÷	3	=	1
	=	12	÷	3
5	=		÷	3
6	=		÷	3
	=	21	÷	3
8	=		÷	3
10	x	3	=	

Set 7				
	÷	3	=	9
30	÷	3	=	
	÷	3	=	11
36	÷	3	=	
	=	3	÷	3
2	=		÷	3
3	=		÷	3
11	x	3	=	
	=	10	x	3
33	=		x	3

Set 8				
15	÷	3	=	
	=	9	÷	3
	x	3	=	33
27	=		x	3
9	=		x	3
	÷	3	=	8
24	=		x	3
4	x	3	=	
	x	3	=	15
8	x	3	=	

Set 9				
4	=		÷	3
	x	3	=	36
3	=		x	3
	=	2	x	3
9	=		÷	3
	=	30	÷	3
	=	10	x	3
33	=		x	3
	x	3	=	6
21	÷	3	=	

Times Tables Ninja © Sarah Farrell, 2022

3

1 Complete the maze by drawing a line through multiples of 3. Watch out for dead ends!

START HERE

3	6	9	1	22	31	5	24	9	7	9	1	2
22	1	12	22	16	15	26	3	8	22	3	4	18
26	19	33	31	35	3	6	21	24	29	28	11	22
29	15	36	18	12	15	7	8	18	30	33	19	16
32	4	17	29	6	13	8	3	13	19	36	22	17
23	7	15	8	21	11	12	19	22	22	6	36	10
32	2	19	9	29	16	19	22	16	34	9	17	12
21	17	28	2	25	22	20	18	13	15	12	19	17
31	23	36	6	19	17	22	15	9	21	23	27	22
17	6	27	8	13	10	25	4	2	18	22	29	28
18	8	23	1	12	19	27	1	11	24	36	9	**EXIT**

2 Fill in the gaps in the table.

a	3 + 3	1 x 3	3
b		6 x 3	18
c	3 + 3 + 3 + 3 + 3 + 3 + 3 + 3		
d			36
e	3 + 3		6
f		5 x 3	
g			33
h	3 + 3 + 3 + 3 + 3 + 3 + 3	7 x 3	
i		3 x 3	9
j	3 + 3 + 3 + 3 + 3 + 3 + 3 + 3 + 3 + 3	10 x 3	
k			12
l	3 + 3 + 3 + 3 + 3 + 3 + 3 + 3 + 3		

4

1 Calculate the area of each of these rectangles (not drawn to scale).

3 cm

6 cm² | 2 cm

3 cm x 2 cm = 6 cm²

a
3 cm
1 cm

b
12 cm
3 cm

c
3 cm
3 cm

d
3 cm
5 cm

e
4 cm
3 cm

f
3 cm
9 cm

g
10 cm
3 cm

h
3 cm
7 cm

i
6 cm
3 cm

j
3 cm
8 cm

k
3 cm
11 cm

2 Find the area of rectangles with these measurements.

a	50 cm long and 3 cm wide	
b	30 cm long and 12 cm wide	
c	3 cm long and 40 cm wide	

Ninja Challenge

1 Use the known multiplication facts to answer these questions.

Example

1 x 3 =	3
10 x 3 =	30
100 x 3 =	300

a

2 x 3 =	
20 x 3 =	
200 x 3 =	

b

3 x 3 =	
30 x 3 =	
300 x 3 =	

c

4 x 3 =	
40 x 3 =	
400 x 3 =	

d

5 x 3 =	
50 x 3 =	
500 x 3 =	

e

6 x 3 =	
60 x 3 =	
600 x 3 =	

f

7 x 3 =	
70 x 3 =	
700 x 3 =	

g

8 x 3 =	
80 x 3 =	
800 x 3 =	

h

9 x 3 =	
90 x 3 =	
900 x 3 =	

i

10 x 3 =	
100 x 3 =	
1,000 x 3 =	

j

11 x 3 =	
110 x 3 =	
1,100 x 3 =	

k

12 x 3 =	
120 x 3 =	
1,200 x 3 =	

2 Use the known multiplication facts to answer these questions.

Example

36 x 3	
30 x 3	90
6 x 3	18
Total:	108

a

28 x 3	
20 x 3	
8 x 3	
Total:	

b

75 x 3	
70 x 3	
5 x 3	
Total:	

c

39 x 3	
30 x 3	
9 x 3	
Total:	

d

57 x 3	
50 x 3	
7 x 3	
Total:	

e

48 x 3	
40 x 3	
8 x 3	
Total:	

f

284 x 3	
200 x 3	
80 x 3	
4 x 3	
Total:	

g

472 x 3	
400 x 3	
70 x 3	
2 x 3	
Total:	

h

395 x 3	
300 x 3	
90 x 3	
5 x 3	
Total:	

6

Complete these short division questions using the 3 times table.

Example

$$411 \div 3 = 137$$

```
        1   3   7
   3 | 4  ¹1  ²1
```

You could write out the times table to help you with these questions.

1
```
3 | 7   9   5
```

2
```
3 | 4   0   5
```

3
```
3 | 7   5   9
```

4
```
3 | 6   9   3
```

5
```
3 | 7   2   3
```

6
```
3 | 8   2   8
```

7
```
3 | 7   0   5
```

8
```
3 | 7   5   3
```

9
```
3 | 7   2   9
```

10	1,002	÷	3	=
11	258	÷	3	=
12	372	÷	3	=
13	234	÷	3	=

14	1,068	÷	3	=
15	1,758	÷	3	=
16	1,638	÷	3	=
17	2,568	÷	3	=

Calculations

Use this space for jottings and written calculations.

Times Tables Ninja © Sarah Farrell, 2022

Write the multiplication or division calculation and answer for each of these word problems.

1	Some stools have 3 legs each. How many legs will 8 stools have?	
2	A triangle has 3 angles. How many angles will 12 triangles have?	
3	A teacher puts children into groups of 3. How many groups will be needed for 9 children?	
4	A child shares 18 toys equally into 3 different piles. How many toys will there be in each pile?	
5	Mia, Sinead and Lucas have £11 each. How much money do they have altogether?	
6	2 sets of triplets go to the swimming pool. How many children are there in total?	
7	A group of 9 children each read 3 books. How many books do they read in total?	
8	There are 3 identical cushions on a chair. Each one has 10 stripes. How many stripes are there in total?	
9	A dad shares £24 equally between his 3 children. How much will they get each?	
10	120 children are put equally into 3 teams. How many children will be in each team?	
11	3 children raise £120 each for charity. How much do they raise in total?	
12	A tricycle has 3 wheels. If a factory has 180 wheels, how many tricycles can be made?	
13	In Year 5, there are 3 classes of 30 children. How many children are there in Year 5 in total?	
14	3 children share a bag of 240 marbles equally between themselves. How many will they receive each?	

8

Use the 3 times table to find these equivalent fractions.

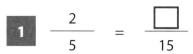

$$\frac{3}{24} = \frac{1}{8}$$ ÷3, ÷3

$$\frac{1}{5} = \frac{3}{15}$$ x3, x3

Example

Multiply or divide the numerator and the denominator by the same number.

1 $\frac{2}{5} = \frac{\Box}{15}$

2 $\frac{21}{24} = \frac{7}{\Box}$

3 $\frac{2}{7} = \frac{\Box}{21}$

4 $\frac{33}{36} = \frac{11}{\Box}$

5 $\frac{12}{15} = \frac{\Box}{5}$

6 $\frac{18}{21} = \frac{6}{\Box}$

7 $\frac{9}{33} = \frac{\Box}{11}$

8 $\frac{7}{8} = \frac{\Box}{24}$

9 $\frac{5}{12} = \frac{15}{\Box}$

10 $\frac{\Box}{33} = \frac{3}{11}$

11 $\frac{21}{33} = \frac{7}{\Box}$

12 $\frac{2}{10} = \frac{\Box}{30}$

13 $\frac{2}{\Box} = \frac{6}{33}$

14 $\frac{\Box}{27} = \frac{4}{9}$

15 $\frac{6}{24} = \frac{2}{\Box}$

16 $\frac{10}{11} = \frac{\Box}{33}$

17 $\frac{4}{\Box} = \frac{12}{36}$

18 $\frac{4}{7} = \frac{12}{\Box}$

19 $\frac{8}{11} = \frac{\Box}{33}$

20 $\frac{15}{\Box} = \frac{5}{10}$

21 $\frac{30}{\Box} = \frac{10}{12}$

22 $\frac{5}{7} = \frac{\Box}{21}$

Use the given fraction to find the whole number.

Example

$\dfrac{1}{3}$ of $\boxed{21}$ is 7

7	7	7
21		

1 $\dfrac{1}{3}$ of $\boxed{}$ is 8

8		

2 $\dfrac{1}{3}$ of $\boxed{}$ is 5

5		

3 $\dfrac{1}{3}$ of $\boxed{}$ is 4

4		

4 $\dfrac{1}{3}$ of $\boxed{}$ is 3

3		

5 $\dfrac{1}{3}$ of $\boxed{}$ is 2

2		

6 $\dfrac{1}{3}$ of $\boxed{}$ is 11

11		

7 $\dfrac{1}{3}$ of $\boxed{}$ is 10

10		

8 $\dfrac{1}{3}$ of $\boxed{}$ is 6

6		

9 $\dfrac{1}{3}$ of $\boxed{}$ is 12

10 $\dfrac{1}{3}$ of $\boxed{}$ is 9

11 $\dfrac{1}{3}$ of $\boxed{}$ is 13

12 $\dfrac{1}{3}$ of $\boxed{}$ is 20

13 $\dfrac{1}{3}$ of $\boxed{}$ is 50

14 $\dfrac{1}{3}$ of $\boxed{}$ is 25

15 $\dfrac{1}{3}$ of $\boxed{}$ is 15

16 $\dfrac{1}{3}$ of $\boxed{}$ is 22

17 $\dfrac{1}{3}$ of $\boxed{}$ is 60

18 $\dfrac{1}{3}$ of $\boxed{}$ is 30

Find $\frac{1}{3}$ of the numbers below by dividing them by 3.

Example

$\frac{1}{3}$ of 30 = [10]

10	10	10
30		

1 $\frac{1}{3}$ of 3 = [ ]

2 $\frac{1}{3}$ of 21 = [ ]

3 $\frac{1}{3}$ of 6 = [ ]

4 $\frac{1}{3}$ of 15 = [ ]

5 $\frac{1}{3}$ of 33 = [ ]

6 $\frac{1}{3}$ of 36 = [ ]

7 $\frac{1}{3}$ of 9 = [ ]

8 $\frac{1}{3}$ of 24 = [ ]

9 $\frac{1}{3}$ of 18 = [ ]

10 $\frac{1}{3}$ of 27 = [ ]

11 $\frac{1}{3}$ of 12 = [ ]

12 $\frac{1}{3}$ of 360 = [ ]

13 $\frac{1}{3}$ of 240 = [ ]

14 $\frac{1}{3}$ of 90 = [ ]

15 $\frac{1}{3}$ of 99 = [ ]

16 $\frac{1}{3}$ of 180 = [ ]

17 $\frac{1}{3}$ of 120 = [ ]

18 $\frac{1}{3}$ of 600 = [ ]

Adjust these ingredients lists by the amounts shown. Use the number facts if you need to.

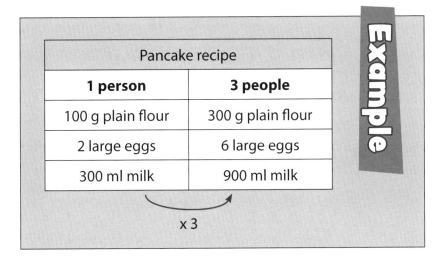

Example

Pancake recipe	
1 person	**3 people**
100 g plain flour	300 g plain flour
2 large eggs	6 large eggs
300 ml milk	900 ml milk

x 3

Multiply or divide each ingredient by the same number to scale the recipe up or down.

1

Milkshake recipe	
2 people	**6 people**
200 ml milk	
3 bananas	
2 chocolate bars	

x 3

2

Flapjack recipe	
1 flapjack traybake	**3 flapjack traybakes**
200 g oats	
120 g butter	
110 g brown sugar	

x 3

3

Fudge recipe	
30 pieces	**10 pieces**
300 g sugar	
360 ml cream	
120 g butter	

÷ 3

4

Rock cakes recipe	
15 rock cakes	**5 rock cakes**
135 g flour	
75 g sugar	
120 g butter	
180 g dried fruit	

÷ 3

5

Smoothie recipe	
1 smoothie	**3 smoothies**
11 strawberries	
9 cherries	
50 ml yoghurt	
100 ml juice	

x 3

Calculations

Use this space for jottings and written calculations.

12

Find the perimeters of these regular polygons (not drawn to scale).

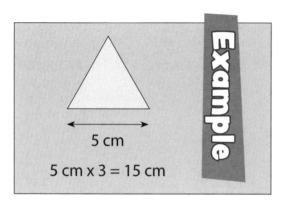

Example

5 cm

5 cm x 3 = 15 cm

Multiply the length of one side by the number of sides to find the perimeter of regular polygons.

1

10 cm

Answer:

2

12 cm

Answer:

3

4 cm

Answer:

4

11 cm

Answer:

5

8 cm

Answer:

6

9 cm

Answer:

7

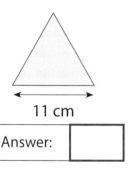

3 cm

Answer:

8

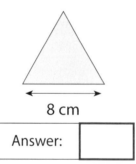

3 cm

Answer:

9

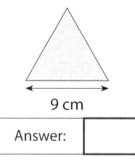

30 cm

Answer:

10

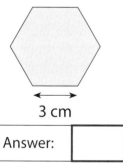

3 cm

Answer:

11

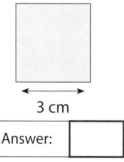

30 cm

Answer:

12

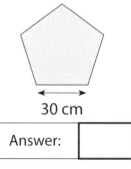

3 cm

Answer:

4 TIMES TABLE

Can you see any patterns in the 4 times table?

1 **Shade in or circle the multiples of 4 up to 100.**

1	2	3	4	5	6	7	8	9	10
11	12	13	14	15	16	17	18	19	20
21	22	23	24	25	26	27	28	29	30
31	32	33	34	35	36	37	38	39	40
41	42	43	44	45	46	47	48	49	50
51	52	53	54	55	56	57	58	59	60
61	62	63	64	65	66	67	68	69	70
71	72	73	74	75	76	77	78	79	80
81	82	83	84	85	86	87	88	89	90
91	92	93	94	95	96	97	98	99	100

2 **Find and circle the 4 times table in this number search.**

1	x	4	=	4	3	6	9	x	4	=	3	4
8	10	x	4	=	40	x	x	x	4	6	x	x
12	x	3	6	x	4	=	24	4	4	24	4	4
x	4	9	x	8	x	4	=	40	8	=	=	=
4	2	5	x	44	5	40	8	44	48	3	36	16
=	8	x	=	4	32	7	x	4	=	28	=	4
48	x	3	4	8	=	44	4	8	x	4	5	3
12	5	x	4	=	20	32	=	12	x	4	=	44
5	x	4	=	25	8	4	32	11	x	4	=	14
3	x	4	=	11	2	x	8	x	4	=	24	12
11	x	4	=	44	8	x	4	3	x	4	=	12

Fill in the missing numbers.

Set 1

1	x	4	=	
	x	4	=	40
	x	4	=	44
28	=		x	4
	=	8	x	4
2	=		÷	4
	÷	4	=	9
	÷	4	=	6
20	÷	4	=	
5	x	4	=	

Set 2

16	=		x	4
	=	9	x	4
	÷	4	=	10
	x	4	=	16
16	÷	4	=	
	=	10	x	4
	÷	4	=	3
	=	24	÷	4
	=	28	÷	4
8	=		÷	4

Set 3

12	x	4	=	
	÷	4	=	7
10	=		÷	4
	x	4	=	32
9	x	4	=	
	÷	4	=	11
48	÷	4	=	
	=	4	÷	4
	=	36	÷	4
24	=		x	4

Set 4

48	=		x	4
	÷	4	=	1
8	÷	4	=	
	=	12	÷	4
	=	2	x	4
12	=		x	4
3	x	4	=	
	÷	4	=	8
11	=		÷	4
12	=		÷	4

Set 5

	=	44	÷	4
12	=		÷	4
44	=		x	4
2	x	4	=	
	x	4	=	24
	=	5	x	4
7	x	4	=	
	=	16	÷	4
5	=		÷	4
4	=		x	4

Set 6

10	=		÷	4
8	x	4	=	
	x	4	=	36
44	÷	4	=	
	÷	4	=	12
36	÷	4	=	
	÷	4	=	6
	÷	4	=	5
5	x	4	=	
	=	4	x	4

Set 7

4	÷	4	=	
	÷	4	=	2
3	=		÷	4
	=	2	x	4
12	=		x	4
	x	4	=	12
32	÷	4	=	
	=	44	÷	4
12	=		÷	4
36	÷	4	=	

Set 8

	÷	4	=	2
3	=		÷	4
	=	2	x	4
12	=		x	4
3	x	4	=	
	÷	4	=	8
	=	44	÷	4
12	=		÷	4
	=	11	x	4
	x	4	=	8

Set 9

28	=		x	4
	=	8	x	4
2	=		÷	4
	÷	4	=	9
	÷	4	=	6
20	÷	4	=	
	x	4	=	20
	=	4	x	4
36	=		x	4
	÷	4	=	10

4 TIMES TABLE

1 **Complete the maze by drawing a line through multiples of 4. Watch out for dead ends!**

START HERE

4	1	8	14	26	37	48	45	18	2	29	4	14
12	5	18	12	26	32	36	24	16	25	6	24	45
16	7	25	36	37	34	21	11	17	15	19	27	22
8	17	36	25	38	14	31	25	26	32	35	21	18
32	10	21	22	41	16	42	31	42	34	29	31	40
36	19	7	22	23	12	16	18	21	13	9	25	28
44	23	12	36	48	4	5	26	16	18	19	20	23
48	18	15	32	33	8	25	38	15	18	22	18	6
12	16	20	24	38	12	26	13	7	40	44	11	22
20	34	26	29	30	16	34	38	8	36	27	30	7
42	48	36	24	9	32	40	44	48	16	12	32	**EXIT**

2 **Fill in the gaps in the table.**

a	4 + 4 + 4 + 4 + 4 + 4	6 x 4	24
b	4 + 4		
c	4 + 4 + 4 + 4 + 4 + 4 + 4 + 4 + 4 + 4 + 4		44
d	4 + 4 + 4 + 4 + 4 + 4 + 4		28
e	4		4
f		12 x 4	48
g	4 + 4 + 4 + 4 + 4 + 4 + 4 + 4		32
h	4 + 4 + 4 + 4 + 4	5 x 4	
i		10 x 4	40
j		3 x 4	
k			16
l	4 + 4 + 4 + 4 + 4 + 4 + 4 + 4 + 4		

1 Calculate the area of each of these rectangles (not drawn to scale).

12 cm

48 cm²

4 cm   12 cm x 4 cm = 48 cm²

a 4 cm / 1 cm

b 4 cm / 4 cm

c 4 cm / 2 cm

d 4 cm / 3 cm

e 5 cm / 4 cm

f 9 cm / 4 cm

g 4 cm / 8 cm

h 10 cm / 4 cm

i 4 cm / 7 cm

j 6 cm / 4 cm

k 4 cm / 11 cm

2 Find the area of rectangles with these measurements.

Ninja Challenge

a	30 cm long and 4 cm wide	
b	40 cm long and 8 cm wide	
c	4 cm long and 40 cm wide	

4 TIMES TABLE

1 Use the known multiplication facts to answer these questions.

Example

1 x 4 =	4
10 x 4 =	40
100 x 4 =	400

a

2 x 4 =	
20 x 4 =	
200 x 4 =	

b

3 x 4 =	
30 x 4 =	
300 x 4 =	

c

4 x 4 =	
40 x 4 =	
400 x 4 =	

d

5 x 4 =	
50 x 4 =	
500 x 4 =	

e

6 x 4 =	
60 x 4 =	
600 x 4 =	

f

7 x 4 =	
70 x 4 =	
700 x 4 =	

g

8 x 4 =	
80 x 4 =	
800 x 4 =	

h

9 x 4 =	
90 x 4 =	
900 x 4 =	

i

10 x 4 =	
100 x 4 =	
1,000 x 4 =	

j

11 x 4 =	
110 x 4 =	
1,100 x 4 =	

k

12 x 4 =	
120 x 4 =	
1,200 x 4 =	

2 Use the known multiplication facts to answer these questions.

Example

36 x 4	
30 x 4	120
6 x 4	24
Total:	144

a

28 x 4	
20 x 4	
8 x 4	
Total:	

b

75 x 4	
70 x 4	
5 x 4	
Total:	

c

39 x 4	
30 x 4	
9 x 4	
Total:	

d

57 x 4	
50 x 4	
7 x 4	
Total:	

e

48 x 4	
40 x 4	
8 x 4	
Total:	

f

284 x 4	
200 x 4	
80 x 4	
4 x 4	
Total:	

g

472 x 4	
400 x 4	
70 x 4	
2 x 4	
Total:	

h

395 x 4	
300 x 4	
90 x 4	
5 x 4	
Total:	

6

Complete these short division questions using the 4 times table.

Example

$784 \div 4 = 196$

```
      1   9   6
  4 | 7  ³8  ²4
```

You could write out the times table to help you with these questions.

1
```
  4 | 9  4  0
```

2
```
  4 | 3  9  2
```

3
```
  4 | 9  2  4
```

4
```
  4 | 6  6  0
```

5
```
  4 | 9  6  4
```

6
```
  4 | 6  7  2
```

7
```
  4 | 9  4  4
```

8
```
  4 | 5  4  4
```

9
```
  4 | 5  8  4
```

10	1,188	÷	4	=
11	1,024	÷	4	=
12	316	÷	4	=
13	2,592	÷	4	=

14	2,372	÷	4	=
15	1,380	÷	4	=
16	3,424	÷	4	=
17	2,796	÷	4	=

Calculations

Use this space for jottings and written calculations.

Write the multiplication or division calculation and answer for each of these word problems.

1	Cakes come in packs of 4. How many packs will be needed for 28 children to have 1 each?	
2	Chairs have 4 legs. How many legs will 12 chairs have?	
3	Some counters are sorted into piles of 4. If there are 8 piles, how many counters are there in total?	
4	Some pencils are sorted equally into 4 pots. If there are 44 pencils in total, how many will be put into each pot?	
5	Pens are sold in packs of 4. How many pens will there be in 9 packs?	
6	4 children each have £4. How much money do they have altogether?	
7	Books are placed on 4 shelves. If there are 10 books on each shelf, how many books are there in total?	
8	Notebooks are sold in sets of 4. Cameron needs to buy 20 notebooks. How many sets will he need?	
9	Maisie has 4 bags, which each have the same number of marbles in them. If there are 36 marbles in total, how many marbles are in each bag?	
10	A group of 240 people are put equally into 4 teams. How many people will there be in each team?	
11	80 cakes are each cut into quarters. How many pieces of cake are there?	
12	80 grapes are split evenly into 4 bowls. How many grapes will there be in each bowl?	
13	200 children each donate £4 to charity. How much money is raised altogether?	
14	A class of 30 children each make 4 paper flowers. How many paper flowers do they make altogether?	

8

Use the 4 times table to find these equivalent fractions.

 Multiply or divide the numerator and the denominator by the same number.

1 $\dfrac{2}{5} = \dfrac{8}{\square}$

2 $\dfrac{28}{32} = \dfrac{\square}{8}$

3 $\dfrac{2}{7} = \dfrac{8}{\square}$

4 $\dfrac{44}{48} = \dfrac{\square}{12}$

5 $\dfrac{12}{16} = \dfrac{3}{\square}$

6 $\dfrac{\square}{28} = \dfrac{6}{7}$

7 $\dfrac{12}{44} = \dfrac{\square}{11}$

8 $\dfrac{5}{11} = \dfrac{20}{\square}$

9 $\dfrac{6}{12} = \dfrac{24}{\square}$

10 $\dfrac{4}{\square} = \dfrac{1}{10}$

11 $\dfrac{20}{44} = \dfrac{\square}{11}$

12 $\dfrac{1}{\square} = \dfrac{4}{36}$

13 $\dfrac{2}{11} = \dfrac{\square}{44}$

14 $\dfrac{28}{32} = \dfrac{7}{\square}$

15 $\dfrac{4}{\square} = \dfrac{1}{7}$

16 $\dfrac{\square}{9} = \dfrac{24}{36}$

17 $\dfrac{11}{12} = \dfrac{44}{\square}$

18 $\dfrac{5}{7} = \dfrac{\square}{28}$

19 $\dfrac{8}{11} = \dfrac{\square}{44}$

20 $\dfrac{\square}{32} = \dfrac{6}{8}$

21 $\dfrac{\square}{44} = \dfrac{10}{11}$

22 $\dfrac{4}{12} = \dfrac{16}{\square}$

Use the given fraction to find the whole number.

Example

$\dfrac{1}{4}$ of [28] is 7

7	7	7	7
28			

1 $\dfrac{1}{4}$ of [ ] is 8

8			

2 $\dfrac{1}{4}$ of [ ] is 5

5			

3 $\dfrac{1}{4}$ of [ ] is 4

4			

4 $\dfrac{1}{4}$ of [ ] is 3

3			

5 $\dfrac{1}{4}$ of [ ] is 2

2			

6 $\dfrac{1}{4}$ of [ ] is 11

11			

7 $\dfrac{1}{4}$ of [ ] is 10

10			

8 $\dfrac{1}{4}$ of [ ] is 6

6			

---

9 $\dfrac{1}{4}$ of [ ] is 12

10 $\dfrac{1}{4}$ of [ ] is 9

11 $\dfrac{1}{4}$ of [ ] is 13

12 $\dfrac{1}{4}$ of [ ] is 20

13 $\dfrac{1}{4}$ of [ ] is 50

14 $\dfrac{1}{4}$ of [ ] is 25

15 $\dfrac{1}{4}$ of [ ] is 30

16 $\dfrac{1}{4}$ of [ ] is 15

17 $\dfrac{1}{4}$ of [ ] is 22

18 $\dfrac{1}{4}$ of [ ] is 40

Find $\frac{1}{4}$ of the numbers below by dividing them by 4.

Example

$\frac{1}{4}$ of 40 = 10

10	10	10	10
40			

1 $\frac{1}{4}$ of 20 =

2 $\frac{1}{4}$ of 32 =

3 $\frac{1}{4}$ of 16 =

4 $\frac{1}{4}$ of 48 =

5 $\frac{1}{4}$ of 12 =

6 $\frac{1}{4}$ of 4 =

7 $\frac{1}{4}$ of 28 =

8 $\frac{1}{4}$ of 36 =

9 $\frac{1}{4}$ of 8 =

10 $\frac{1}{4}$ of 24 =

11 $\frac{1}{4}$ of 44 =

12 $\frac{1}{4}$ of 80 =

13 $\frac{1}{4}$ of 120 =

14 $\frac{1}{4}$ of 280 =

15 $\frac{1}{4}$ of 400 =

16 $\frac{1}{4}$ of 320 =

17 $\frac{1}{4}$ of 440 =

18 $\frac{1}{4}$ of 1,000 =

Adjust these ingredients lists by the amounts shown. Use the number facts if you need to.

Example

Pancake recipe	
1 person	**4 people**
100 g plain flour	400 g plain flour
2 large eggs	8 large eggs
300 ml milk	1,200 ml milk

x 4

Multiply or divide each ingredient by the same number to scale the recipe up or down.

1

Milkshake recipe	
2 people	**8 people**
200 ml milk	
3 bananas	
2 chocolate bars	

x 4

2

Flapjack recipe	
1 flapjack traybake	**4 flapjack traybakes**
200 g oats	
120 g butter	
110 g brown sugar	

x 4

3

Fudge recipe	
48 pieces	**12 pieces**
440 g sugar	
400 ml cream	
48 g butter	

÷ 4

4

Rock cakes recipe	
16 rock cakes	**4 rock cakes**
240 g flour	
60 g sugar	
120 g butter	
160 g dried fruit	

÷ 4

5

Smoothie recipe	
1 smoothie	**4 smoothies**
11 strawberries	
9 cherries	
50 ml yoghurt	
100 ml juice	

x 4

Calculations

Use this space for jottings and written calculations.

Find the perimeters of these regular polygons (not drawn to scale).

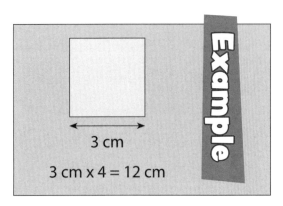

Example

3 cm

3 cm x 4 = 12 cm

Multiply the length of one side by the number of sides to find the perimeter of regular polygons.

1
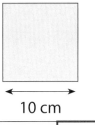
10 cm
Answer:

2

12 cm
Answer:

3

4 cm
Answer:

4
11 cm
Answer:

5
8 cm
Answer:

6
9 cm
Answer:

7
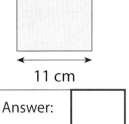
4 cm
Answer:

8
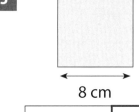
4 cm
Answer:

9
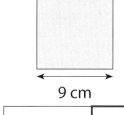
4 cm
Answer:

10
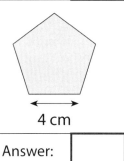
4 cm
Answer:

11
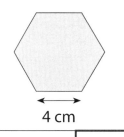
40 cm
Answer:

12
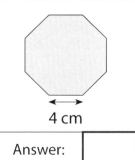
40 cm
Answer:

1

Can you see any patterns in the 5 times table?

1 Shade in or circle the multiples of 5 up to 100.

1	2	3	4	5	6	7	8	9	10
11	12	13	14	15	16	17	18	19	20
21	22	23	24	25	26	27	28	29	30
31	32	33	34	35	36	37	38	39	40
41	42	43	44	45	46	47	48	49	50
51	52	53	54	55	56	57	58	59	60
61	62	63	64	65	66	67	68	69	70
71	72	73	74	75	76	77	78	79	80
81	82	83	84	85	86	87	88	89	90
91	92	93	94	95	96	97	98	99	100

2 Find and circle the 5 times table in this number search.

1	x	5	=	5	3	x	5	=	2	11	7	3
2	8	x	5	=	40	12	4	6	x	5	=	30
10	x	5	=	5	8	5	=	45	5	x	4	x
8	x	5	6	3	x	x	30	5	=	5	x	5
x	4	5	=	x	3	5	5	1	10	=	5	=
5	5	x	=	4	x	5	=	20	2	30	8	15
3	9	3	=	50	5	4	x	25	=	20	4	12
6	x	5	=	25	=	11	7	x	5	=	30	x
x	5	5	6	3	10	7	x	5	=	35	3	5
6	=	5	=	30	8	x	5	5	11	x	5	=
5	45	6	x	15	5	=	11	x	5	=	55	60

Fill in the missing numbers.

Set 1

	x	5	=	5
2	x	5	=	
	÷	5	=	1
	÷	5	=	2
60	÷	5	=	
30	=		x	5
	=	7	x	5
	=	8	x	5
12	x	5	=	
5	=		x	5

Set 2

25	=		x	5
40	÷	5	=	
	=	9	x	5
	=	15	÷	5
4	=		÷	5
	=	25	÷	5
	x	5	=	45
10	x	5	=	
45	÷	5	=	
	x	5	=	30

Set 3

	x	5	=	35
8	x	5	=	
	=	10	x	5
	=	11	x	5
	x	5	=	55
6	=		÷	5
	=	2	x	5
	=	3	x	5
7	=		÷	5
	=	40	÷	5

Set 4

9	=		÷	5
	÷	5	=	10
55	÷	5	=	
	=	4	x	5
11	=		÷	5
12	=		÷	5
3	x	5	=	
	x	5	=	20
	x	5	=	25
15	÷	5	=	

Set 5

4	x	5	=	
	x	5	=	25
	÷	5	=	3
20	÷	5	=	
	÷	5	=	5
	=	5	÷	5
2	=		÷	5
30	÷	5	=	
	÷	5	=	7
10	=		÷	5

Set 6

7	=		÷	5
8	=		÷	5
	=	45	÷	5
50	÷	5	=	
	÷	5	=	11
30	=		x	5
	=	7	x	5
40	=		x	5
12	x	5	=	
	=	1	x	5

Set 7

3	x	5	=	
	=	10	x	5
55	=		x	5
	x	5	=	55
6	=		÷	5
	=	8	x	5
12	x	5	=	
	=	1	x	5
25	=		x	5
	÷	5	=	3

Set 8

	=	8	x	5
12	x	5	=	
	=	1	x	5
20	÷	5	=	
25	÷	5	=	
	=	5	÷	5
2	=		÷	5
	÷	5	=	6
15	=		x	5
	÷	5	=	8

Set 9

	=	40	÷	5
9	=		÷	5
45	=		x	5
50	÷	5	=	
	÷	5	=	11
	=	4	x	5
	=	55	÷	5
12	=		÷	5
45	÷	5	=	
	x	5	=	30

5 TIMES TABLE

1 Complete the maze by drawing a line through multiples of 5. Watch out for dead ends!

START HERE

5	20	43	37	18	37	21	62	43	55	68	28	40
23	25	62	26	31	43	72	28	11	32	40	42	14
45	30	45	15	20	5	15	17	21	58	30	45	23
16	11	21	40	17	11	32	15	27	21	36	54	50
27	22	53	60	26	54	38	84	14	20	31	40	35
38	42	27	55	10	20	40	31	12	15	16	30	25
32	26	38	2	25	28	55	45	30	35	15	67	32
43	42	42	5	30	37	19	26	43	25	47	62	54
46	57	49	2	45	42	2	32	31	15	20	40	50
74	54	1	3	12	32	32	45	11	26	15	16	60
56	23	5	6	23	18	54	70	10	18	9	10	**EXIT**

2 Fill in the gaps in the table.

a	5 + 5 + 5 + 5 + 5 + 5 + 5	7 x 5	35
b		4 x 5	20
c	5 + 5 + 5 + 5 + 5 + 5		
d			55
e	5 + 5		10
f		8 x 5	
g	5 + 5 + 5 + 5 + 5 + 5 + 5 + 5 + 5 + 5 + 5 + 5		
h			5
i		10 x 5	
j	5 + 5 + 5 + 5 + 5	5 x 5	
k			45
l	5 + 5 + 5		

1 Calculate the area of each of these rectangles (not drawn to scale).

Example

5 cm

10 cm² | 2 cm

2 cm x 5 cm = 10 cm²

a 12 cm | 5 cm

b 5 cm | 5 cm

c 5 cm | 9 cm

d 1 cm | 5 cm

e 3 cm | 5 cm

f 5 cm | 10 cm

g 5 cm | 8 cm

h 7 cm | 5 cm

i 6 cm | 5 cm

j 5 cm | 4 cm

k 5 cm | 11 cm

2 Find the area of rectangles with these measurements.

Ninja Challenge

a	50 cm long and 5 cm wide	
b	50 cm long and 12 cm wide	
c	5 cm long and 40 cm wide	

1 Use the known multiplication facts to answer these questions.

Example

1 x 5 =	5
10 x 5 =	50
100 x 5 =	500

a

2 x 5 =	
20 x 5 =	
200 x 5 =	

b

3 x 5 =	
30 x 5 =	
300 x 5 =	

c

4 x 5 =	
40 x 5 =	
400 x 5 =	

d

5 x 5 =	
50 x 5 =	
500 x 5 =	

e

6 x 5 =	
60 x 5 =	
600 x 5 =	

f

7 x 5 =	
70 x 5 =	
700 x 5 =	

g

8 x 5 =	
80 x 5 =	
800 x 5 =	

h

9 x 5 =	
90 x 5 =	
900 x 5 =	

i

10 x 5 =	
100 x 5 =	
1,000 x 5 =	

j

11 x 5 =	
110 x 5 =	
1,100 x 5 =	

k

12 x 5 =	
120 x 5 =	
1,200 x 5 =	

2 Use the known multiplication facts to answer these questions.

Example

36 x 5	
30 x 5	150
6 x 5	30
Total:	180

a

28 x 5	
20 x 5	
8 x 5	
Total:	

b

75 x 5	
70 x 5	
5 x 5	
Total:	

c

39 x 5	
30 x 5	
9 x 5	
Total:	

d

57 x 5	
50 x 5	
7 x 5	
Total:	

e

48 x 5	
40 x 5	
8 x 5	
Total:	

f

284 x 5	
200 x 5	
80 x 5	
4 x 5	
Total:	

g

472 x 5	
400 x 5	
70 x 5	
2 x 5	
Total:	

h

395 x 5	
300 x 5	
90 x 5	
5 x 5	
Total:	

6

Complete these short division questions using the 5 times table.

$785 \div 5 = 157$

```
        1    5    7
   5 | 7   ²8   ³5
```

You could write out the times table to help you with these questions.

1

```
   5 | 3    2    5
```

2

```
   5 | 5    6    5
```

3

```
   5 | 4    6    5
```

4

```
   5 | 1    5    5
```

5

```
   5 | 3    2    5
```

6

```
   5 | 8    6    5
```

7

```
   5 | 7    3    5
```

8

```
   5 | 2    1    5
```

9

```
   5 | 5    3    5
```

10	675	÷	5	=
11	455	÷	5	=
12	365	÷	5	=
13	5,535	÷	5	=

14	3,465	÷	5	=
15	1,645	÷	5	=
16	5,635	÷	5	=
17	6,765	÷	5	=

Calculations

Use this space for jottings and written calculations.

Write the multiplication or division calculation and answer for each of these word problems.

1	One foot has 5 toes. How many toes will there be on 8 feet?	
2	Grace shares 15 toys equally between 5 piles. How many toys will there be in each pile?	
3	10 children each have £5. How much do they have altogether?	
4	A boy shares 5 apples between 5 bowls. How many apples will be in each bowl?	
5	A pentagon has 5 angles. How many angles will there be in 9 pentagons?	
6	Bananas come in bunches of 5. How many bananas will there be in 12 bunches?	
7	A group of children are put into equal groups of 5. If there are 6 groups, how many children are there in total?	
8	A group of children are put into equal groups of 5. If there are 20 children, how many groups will there be?	
9	5 children each have 5 chocolate bars. How many chocolate bars are there in total?	
10	A group of 5 women share £500 equally between themselves. How much will they receive each?	
11	The 5 classes in a school raise £70 each. How much do they raise altogether?	
12	A group of 550 people are split into 5 teams. How many people will be in each team?	
13	5 children each score 120 points in a game. How many points do they score in total?	
14	A box of 400 pencils is split evenly between 5 classes. How many pencils will each class receive?	

8

Use the 5 times table to find these equivalent fractions.

Multiply or divide the numerator and the denominator by the same number.

Example

$$\xrightarrow{\div 5}$$
$$\frac{5}{25} = \frac{1}{5}$$
$$\xrightarrow{\div 5}$$

$$\xrightarrow{\times 5}$$
$$\frac{1}{5} = \frac{5}{25}$$
$$\xrightarrow{\times 5}$$

1 $\dfrac{2}{\square} = \dfrac{10}{25}$

2 $\dfrac{\square}{40} = \dfrac{7}{8}$

3 $\dfrac{2}{\square} = \dfrac{10}{35}$

4 $\dfrac{55}{60} = \dfrac{\square}{12}$

5 $\dfrac{10}{15} = \dfrac{2}{\square}$

6 $\dfrac{30}{35} = \dfrac{\square}{7}$

7 $\dfrac{15}{55} = \dfrac{\square}{11}$

8 $\dfrac{4}{\square} = \dfrac{20}{45}$

9 $\dfrac{3}{11} = \dfrac{\square}{55}$

10 $\dfrac{5}{40} = \dfrac{1}{\square}$

11 $\dfrac{20}{55} = \dfrac{4}{\square}$

12 $\dfrac{\square}{6} = \dfrac{5}{30}$

13 $\dfrac{2}{\square} = \dfrac{10}{55}$

14 $\dfrac{35}{40} = \dfrac{\square}{8}$

15 $\dfrac{5}{25} = \dfrac{1}{\square}$

16 $\dfrac{\square}{11} = \dfrac{30}{55}$

17 $\dfrac{11}{12} = \dfrac{55}{\square}$

18 $\dfrac{4}{7} = \dfrac{\square}{35}$

19 $\dfrac{8}{11} = \dfrac{40}{\square}$

20 $\dfrac{\square}{30} = \dfrac{5}{6}$

21 $\dfrac{50}{55} = \dfrac{10}{\square}$

22 $\dfrac{5}{9} = \dfrac{\square}{45}$

Use the given fraction to find the whole number.

Example

$\dfrac{1}{5}$ of $\boxed{35}$ is 7

7	7	7	7	7
35				

1 $\dfrac{1}{5}$ of $\boxed{}$ is 8

8				

2 $\dfrac{1}{5}$ of $\boxed{}$ is 5

5				

3 $\dfrac{1}{5}$ of $\boxed{}$ is 4

4				

4 $\dfrac{1}{5}$ of $\boxed{}$ is 3

3				

5 $\dfrac{1}{5}$ of $\boxed{}$ is 2

2				

6 $\dfrac{1}{5}$ of $\boxed{}$ is 11

11				

7 $\dfrac{1}{5}$ of $\boxed{}$ is 10

10				

8 $\dfrac{1}{5}$ of $\boxed{}$ is 6

6				

9 $\dfrac{1}{5}$ of $\boxed{}$ is 12

10 $\dfrac{1}{5}$ of $\boxed{}$ is 9

11 $\dfrac{1}{5}$ of $\boxed{}$ is 13

12 $\dfrac{1}{5}$ of $\boxed{}$ is 20

13 $\dfrac{1}{5}$ of $\boxed{}$ is 50

14 $\dfrac{1}{5}$ of $\boxed{}$ is 25

15 $\dfrac{1}{5}$ of $\boxed{}$ is 90

16 $\dfrac{1}{5}$ of $\boxed{}$ is 22

17 $\dfrac{1}{5}$ of $\boxed{}$ is 100

18 $\dfrac{1}{5}$ of $\boxed{}$ is 200

Find $\frac{1}{5}$ of the numbers below by dividing them by 5.

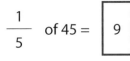

Example

$\frac{1}{5}$ of 45 = **9**

9	9	9	9	9
45				

1 $\frac{1}{5}$ of 5 = ☐

2 $\frac{1}{5}$ of 35 = ☐

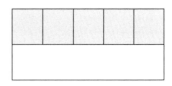

3 $\frac{1}{5}$ of 25 = ☐

4 $\frac{1}{5}$ of 10 = ☐

5 $\frac{1}{5}$ of 55 = ☐

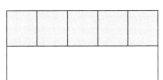

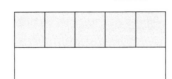

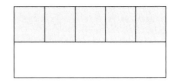

6 $\frac{1}{5}$ of 50 = ☐

7 $\frac{1}{5}$ of 30 = ☐

8 $\frac{1}{5}$ of 20 = ☐

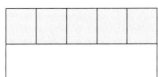

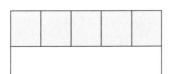

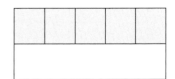

9 $\frac{1}{5}$ of 40 = ☐

14 $\frac{1}{5}$ of 450 = ☐

10 $\frac{1}{5}$ of 15 = ☐

15 $\frac{1}{5}$ of 200 = ☐

11 $\frac{1}{5}$ of 60 = ☐

16 $\frac{1}{5}$ of 350 = ☐

12 $\frac{1}{5}$ of 100 = ☐

17 $\frac{1}{5}$ of 600 = ☐

13 $\frac{1}{5}$ of 300 = ☐

18 $\frac{1}{5}$ of 500 = ☐

Adjust these ingredients lists by the amounts shown. Use the number facts if you need to.

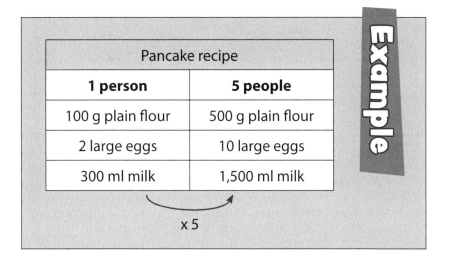

Pancake recipe	
1 person	**5 people**
100 g plain flour	500 g plain flour
2 large eggs	10 large eggs
300 ml milk	1,500 ml milk

x 5

Example

Multiply or divide each ingredient by the same number to scale the recipe up or down.

1

Milkshake recipe	
2 people	**10 people**
200 ml milk	
3 bananas	
2 chocolate bars	

x 5

2

Flapjack recipe	
1 flapjack traybake	**5 flapjack traybakes**
200 g oats	
120 g butter	
110 g brown sugar	

x 5

3

Fudge recipe	
35 pieces	**7 pieces**
450 g sugar	
400 ml cream	
50 g butter	

÷ 5

4

Rock cakes recipe	
15 rock cakes	**3 rock cakes**
225 g flour	
75 g sugar	
125 g butter	
150 g dried fruit	

÷ 5

5

Smoothie recipe	
1 smoothie	**5 smoothies**
11 strawberries	
9 cherries	
50 ml yoghurt	
100 ml juice	

x 5

Calculations

Use this space for jottings and written calculations.

Find the perimeters of these regular polygons (not drawn to scale).

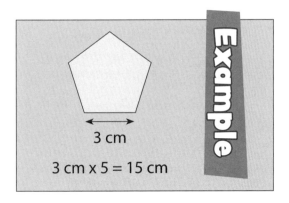

Example

3 cm

3 cm x 5 = 15 cm

Multiply the length of one side by the number of sides to find the perimeter of regular polygons.

1
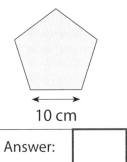

10 cm

Answer:

2

12 cm

Answer:

3

4 cm

Answer:

4
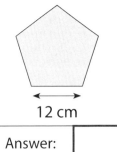

11 cm

Answer:

5

8 cm

Answer:

6
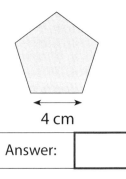

9 cm

Answer:

7
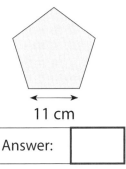

5 cm

Answer:

8
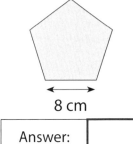

5 cm

Answer:

9
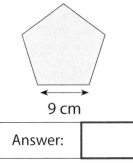

5 cm

Answer:

10
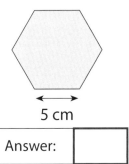

50 cm

Answer:

11
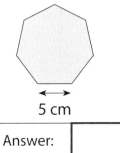

50 cm

Answer:

12
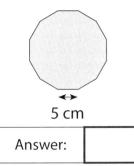

50 cm

Answer:

6 TIMES TABLE

Can you see any patterns in the 6 times table?

1 Shade in or circle the multiples of 6 up to 100.

1	2	3	4	5	6	7	8	9	10
11	12	13	14	15	16	17	18	19	20
21	22	23	24	25	26	27	28	29	30
31	32	33	34	35	36	37	38	39	40
41	42	43	44	45	46	47	48	49	50
51	52	53	54	55	56	57	58	59	60
61	62	63	64	65	66	67	68	69	70
71	72	73	74	75	76	77	78	79	80
81	82	83	84	85	86	87	88	89	90
91	92	93	94	95	96	97	98	99	100

2 Find and circle the 6 times table in this number search.

1	x	6	=	6	3	x	6	=	8	x	12	9
2	3	x	6	=	x	8	x	6	x	11	x	x
x	6	11	12	5	x	6	=	30	6	5	6	7
6	5	x	x	8	x	6	=	60	=	x	=	x
=	9	x	6	6	9	6	x	36	48	6	72	6
12	9	x	6	=	=	x	4	x	6	=	20	=
5	x	6	6	=	16	66	6	x	6	25	11	42
5	8	x	6	=	40	10	x	6	=	60	x	66
3	x	6	=	18	54	9	x	6	=	40	6	72
8	x	12	x	6	=	60	11	x	6	48	=	x
7	x	6	=	36	x	4	x	6	=	24	60	6

Fill in the missing numbers.

Set 1

7	x	6	=	
	÷	6	=	10
	÷	6	=	12
1	=		÷	6
2	=		÷	6
	=	8	x	6
54	=		x	6
	=	12	x	6
60	=		x	6
5	=		÷	6

Set 2

6	=		÷	6
	=	3	x	6
24	=		x	6
	=	5	x	6
6	÷	6	=	
	=	42	÷	6
66	÷	6	=	
	=	48	÷	6
9	=		÷	6
1	x	6	=	

Set 3

3	x	6	=	
42	÷	6	=	
	÷	6	=	8
54	÷	6	=	
	x	6	=	66
12	x	6	=	
	x	6	=	24
5	x	6	=	
	=	6	x	6
42	=		x	6

Set 4

	÷	6	=	3
24	÷	6	=	
30	÷	6	=	
3	=		÷	6
	=	24	÷	6
	x	6	=	48
	=	2	x	6
36	÷	6	=	
9	x	6	=	
10	x	6	=	

Set 5

7	=		÷	6
	÷	6	=	11
8	=		÷	6
	=	54	÷	6
6	=		x	6
	x	6	=	36
11	=		÷	6
12	=		÷	6
	x	6	=	18
	÷	6	=	7

Set 6

	=	6	÷	6
2	=		÷	6
48	=		x	6
	=	9	x	6
72	=		x	6
	x	6	=	66
	x	6	=	72
4	x	6	=	
5	x	6	=	
	=	6	x	6

Set 7

	÷	6	=	3
24	÷	6	=	
	=	11	x	6
12	x	6	=	
	=	10	x	6
	=	30	÷	6
6	=		÷	6
18	=		x	6
	=	4	x	6
30	=		x	6

Set 8

24	=		x	6
18	÷	6	=	
	÷	6	=	4
66	=		x	6
12	÷	6	=	
	=	10	x	6
	=	30	÷	6
6	=		÷	6
	=	3	x	6
30	=		x	6

Set 9

4	=		÷	6
	x	6	=	66
	x	6	=	72
4	x	6	=	
	x	6	=	30
	=	6	x	6
10	=		÷	6
	x	6	=	6
	x	6	=	12
8	x	6	=	

1 Complete the maze by drawing a line through multiples of 6. Watch out for dead ends!

START HERE

6	11	41	33	69	53	26	85	35	47	23	1	60
12	17	19	23	28	72	37	6	24	66	19	18	3
36	18	54	48	36	60	66	8	43	16	3	4	5
31	5	42	4	75	34	60	15	26	13	5	3	24
67	24	60	42	43	18	12	2	24	14	28	34	21
35	4	46	35	57	60	18	8	3	30	42	75	62
27	36	42	22	43	16	6	42	12	18	74	19	25
48	74	57	53	24	46	72	16	61	26	63	11	31
73	25	35	22	89	26	42	18	54	36	30	6	18
35	6	86	11	24	36	67	24	12	3	66	3	72
2	72	37	57	75	22	4	25	64	78	33	6	**EXIT**

2 Fill in the gaps in the table.

a	6 + 6 + 6	3 x 6	18
b	6 + 6 + 6 + 6 + 6 + 6 + 6 + 6		48
c	6 + 6 + 6 + 6 + 6 + 6 + 6 + 6 + 6		
d			24
e		6 x 6	
f	6 + 6 + 6 + 6 + 6 + 6 + 6 + 6 + 6 + 6 + 6 + 6		
g			6
h		7 x 6	
i	6 + 6 + 6 + 6 + 6 + 6 + 6 + 6 + 6 + 6 + 6		66
j		10 x 6	60
k	6 + 6	2 x 6	
l	6 + 6 + 6 + 6 + 6		

1 Calculate the area of each of these rectangles (not drawn to scale).

6 cm

18 cm²   3 cm   6 cm x 3 cm = 18 cm²

a   6 cm   1 cm

b   12 cm   6 cm

c   6 cm   6 cm

d   4 cm   6 cm

e   6 cm   2 cm

f   6 cm   8 cm

g   9 cm   6 cm

h   10 cm   6 cm

i   6 cm   5 cm

j   6 cm   7 cm

k   11 cm   6 cm

2 Find the area of rectangles with these measurements.

a	50 cm long and 6 cm wide	
b	60 cm long and 12 cm wide	
c	6 cm long and 40 cm wide	

Ninja Challenge

1 Use the known multiplication facts to answer these questions.

Example

1 x 6 =	6
10 x 6 =	60
100 x 6 =	600

a

2 x 6 =	
20 x 6 =	
200 x 6 =	

b

3 x 6 =	
30 x 6 =	
300 x 6 =	

c

4 x 6 =	
40 x 6 =	
400 x 6 =	

d

5 x 6 =	
50 x 6 =	
500 x 6 =	

e

6 x 6 =	
60 x 6 =	
600 x 6 =	

f

7 x 6 =	
70 x 6 =	
700 x 6 =	

g

8 x 6 =	
80 x 6 =	
800 x 6 =	

h

9 x 6 =	
90 x 6 =	
900 x 6 =	

i

10 x 6 =	
100 x 6 =	
1,000 x 6 =	

j

11 x 6 =	
110 x 6 =	
1,100 x 6 =	

k

12 x 6 =	
120 x 6 =	
1,200 x 6 =	

2 Use the known multiplication facts to answer these questions.

Example

36 x 6	
30 x 6	180
6 x 6	36
Total:	216

a

28 x 6	
20 x 6	
8 x 6	
Total:	

b

75 x 6	
70 x 6	
5 x 6	
Total:	

c

39 x 6	
30 x 6	
9 x 6	
Total:	

d

57 x 6	
50 x 6	
7 x 6	
Total:	

e

48 x 6	
40 x 6	
8 x 6	
Total:	

f

284 x 6	
200 x 6	
80 x 6	
4 x 6	
Total:	

g

472 x 6	
400 x 6	
70 x 6	
2 x 6	
Total:	

h

395 x 6	
300 x 6	
90 x 6	
5 x 6	
Total:	

Complete these short division questions using the 6 times table.

Example

$786 \div 6 = 131$

```
      1   3   1
  6 | 7  ¹8   6
```

You could write out the times table to help you with these questions.

1
```
  6 | 7   3   8
```

2
```
  6 | 1   5   1   8
```

3
```
  6 | 1   4   4   6
```

4
```
  6 | 5   2   8
```

5
```
  6 | 9   3   6
```

6
```
  6 | 1   9   5   0
```

7
```
  6 | 1   5   2   4
```

8
```
  6 | 2   4   7   2
```

9
```
  6 | 3   1   3   8
```

10	2,214	÷	6	=
11	1,476	÷	6	=
12	1,176	÷	6	=
13	2,106	÷	6	=

14	2,718	÷	6	=
15	2,364	÷	6	=
16	2,850	÷	6	=
17	3,792	÷	6	=

Calculations

Use this space for jottings and written calculations.

Write the multiplication or division calculation and answer for each of these word problems.

1	Bread rolls are sold in packs of 6. How many rolls are there in 8 packs?	
2	Ants have 6 legs. How many legs will 12 ants have?	
3	Tins of soup are sold in packs of 6. If 54 tins of soup are needed, how many packs will need to be bought?	
4	Children are put into groups of 6. How many groups will there be if there are 66 children?	
5	Hexagons have 6 angles. How many angles will there be in 4 hexagons?	
6	6 children share £18 equally between themselves. How much will they have each?	
7	A baker shares 36 g of icing sugar equally between 6 cakes. How much icing sugar will each cake have?	
8	Bananas are sold in bunches of 6. How many bananas will there be in 7 bunches?	
9	6 apples are each cut into 6 pieces. How many pieces of apple will there be in total?	
10	A group of 360 people are put into teams of 6. How many teams will there be?	
11	Apples are sold in bags of 6. If there are 420 apples, how many bags can be filled?	
12	60 g of porridge is needed for one serving. How much will be needed for 8 servings?	
13	A restaurant has tables that seat 6 people. If there are 20 tables, how many people can be seated?	
14	A book has 200 pages. How many pages will 6 books have?	

Use the 6 times table to find these equivalent fractions.

Example

$$\frac{6}{30} = \frac{1}{5} \qquad \frac{1}{6} = \frac{6}{36}$$

$\div 6$ $\times 6$

> Multiply or divide the numerator and the denominator by the same number.

1 $\dfrac{2}{5} = \dfrac{\square}{30}$

2 $\dfrac{42}{\square} = \dfrac{7}{8}$

3 $\dfrac{2}{7} = \dfrac{\square}{42}$

4 $\dfrac{66}{72} = \dfrac{11}{\square}$

5 $\dfrac{\square}{18} = \dfrac{2}{3}$

6 $\dfrac{36}{42} = \dfrac{6}{\square}$

7 $\dfrac{\square}{66} = \dfrac{3}{11}$

8 $\dfrac{4}{8} = \dfrac{\square}{48}$

9 $\dfrac{4}{11} = \dfrac{24}{\square}$

10 $\dfrac{6}{42} = \dfrac{\square}{7}$

11 $\dfrac{\square}{48} = \dfrac{4}{8}$

12 $\dfrac{1}{5} = \dfrac{6}{\square}$

13 $\dfrac{\square}{11} = \dfrac{18}{66}$

14 $\dfrac{42}{48} = \dfrac{\square}{8}$

15 $\dfrac{6}{24} = \dfrac{\square}{4}$

16 $\dfrac{5}{11} = \dfrac{30}{\square}$

17 $\dfrac{10}{12} = \dfrac{\square}{72}$

18 $\dfrac{4}{7} = \dfrac{\square}{42}$

19 $\dfrac{8}{11} = \dfrac{\square}{66}$

20 $\dfrac{36}{48} = \dfrac{6}{\square}$

21 $\dfrac{60}{66} = \dfrac{\square}{11}$

22 $\dfrac{4}{10} = \dfrac{24}{\square}$

Use the given fraction to find the whole number.

Example

$\dfrac{1}{6}$ of [42] is 7

7	7	7	7	7	7
42					

1 $\dfrac{1}{6}$ of [ ] is 8

8					

2 $\dfrac{1}{6}$ of [ ] is 5

5					

3 $\dfrac{1}{6}$ of [ ] is 4

4					

4 $\dfrac{1}{6}$ of [ ] is 3

3					

5 $\dfrac{1}{6}$ of [ ] is 2

2					

6 $\dfrac{1}{6}$ of [ ] is 11

11					

7 $\dfrac{1}{6}$ of [ ] is 10

10					

8 $\dfrac{1}{6}$ of [ ] is 6

6					

9 $\dfrac{1}{6}$ of [ ] is 12

10 $\dfrac{1}{6}$ of [ ] is 9

11 $\dfrac{1}{6}$ of [ ] is 13

12 $\dfrac{1}{6}$ of [ ] is 20

13 $\dfrac{1}{6}$ of [ ] is 50

14 $\dfrac{1}{6}$ of [ ] is 100

15 $\dfrac{1}{6}$ of [ ] is 15

16 $\dfrac{1}{6}$ of [ ] is 30

17 $\dfrac{1}{6}$ of [ ] is 60

18 $\dfrac{1}{6}$ of [ ] is 40

Find $\frac{1}{6}$ of the numbers below by dividing them by 6.

Example

$\frac{1}{6}$ of 42 = 7

7	7	7	7	7	7
42					

1 $\frac{1}{6}$ of 18 =

2 $\frac{1}{6}$ of 54 =

3 $\frac{1}{6}$ of 24 =

4 $\frac{1}{6}$ of 66 =

5 $\frac{1}{6}$ of 30 =

6 $\frac{1}{6}$ of 60 =

7 $\frac{1}{6}$ of 36 =

8 $\frac{1}{6}$ of 48 =

9 $\frac{1}{6}$ of 12 =

10 $\frac{1}{6}$ of 72 =

11 $\frac{1}{6}$ of 6 =

12 $\frac{1}{6}$ of 120 =

13 $\frac{1}{6}$ of 600 =

14 $\frac{1}{6}$ of 240 =

15 $\frac{1}{6}$ of 660 =

16 $\frac{1}{6}$ of 78 =

17 $\frac{1}{6}$ of 180 =

18 $\frac{1}{6}$ of 1,200 =

Adjust these ingredients lists by the amounts shown. Use the number facts if you need to.

Example

Pancake recipe	
1 person	**6 people**
100 g plain flour	600 g plain flour
2 large eggs	12 large eggs
300 ml milk	1,800 ml milk

x 6

Multiply or divide each ingredient by the same number to scale the recipe up or down.

1

Milkshake recipe	
2 people	**12 people**
200 ml milk	
3 bananas	
2 chocolate bars	

x 6

2

Flapjack recipe	
1 flapjack traybake	**6 flapjack traybakes**
200 g oats	
120 g butter	
110 g brown sugar	

x 6

3

Fudge recipe	
36 pieces	**6 pieces**
420 g sugar	
360 ml cream	
48 g butter	

÷ 6

4

Rock cakes recipe	
18 rock cakes	**3 rock cakes**
240 g flour	
72 g sugar	
120 g butter	
180 g dried fruit	

÷ 6

5

Smoothie recipe	
1 smoothie	**6 smoothies**
11 strawberries	
9 cherries	
50 ml yoghurt	
100 ml juice	

x 6

Calculations

Use this space for jottings and written calculations.

Find the perimeters of these regular polygons (not drawn to scale).

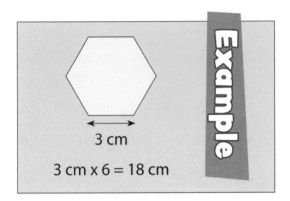

Example

3 cm

3 cm x 6 = 18 cm

Multiply the length of one side by the number of sides to find the perimeter of regular polygons.

1

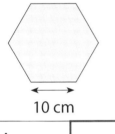

10 cm

Answer:

2

12 cm

Answer:

3

4 cm

Answer:

4

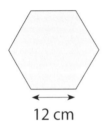

11 cm

Answer:

5

8 cm

Answer:

6

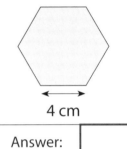

9 cm

Answer:

7

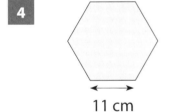

6 cm

Answer:

8

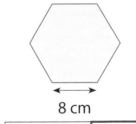

6 cm

Answer:

9

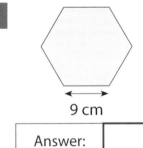

6 cm

Answer:

10

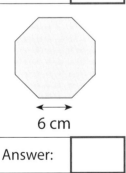

6 cm

Answer:

11

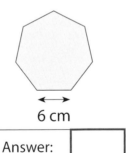

60 cm

Answer:

12

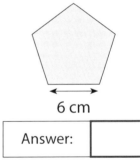

60 cm

Answer:

1  7 TIMES TABLE

1 Shade in or circle the multiples of 7 up to 100.

1	2	3	4	5	6	7	8	9	10
11	12	13	14	15	16	17	18	19	20
21	22	23	24	25	26	27	28	29	30
31	32	33	34	35	36	37	38	39	40
41	42	43	44	45	46	47	48	49	50
51	52	53	54	55	56	57	58	59	60
61	62	63	64	65	66	67	68	69	70
71	72	73	74	75	76	77	78	79	80
81	82	83	84	85	86	87	88	89	90
91	92	93	94	95	96	97	98	99	100

2 Find and circle the 7 times table in this number search.

1	x	7	=	7	70	x	7	42	7	8	56	1
12	77	14	6	x	7	=	42	77	x	x	11	x
9	x	12	x	2	70	3	84	63	7	7	x	7
10	x	7	x	12	x	18	x	14	=	=	7	=
4	x	7	=	7	56	7	28	7	49	63	=	70
x	3	7	63	84	4	35	=	56	=	70	77	12
7	21	7	=	12	x	6	5	14	77	9	84	x
=	84	7	8	70	7	49	x	x	49	x	21	7
21	56	3	x	7	=	21	14	7	7	7	14	=
28	3	x	7	=	28	35	28	42	=	=	70	56
8	x	7	=	56	8	x	7	=	63	63	35	7

Fill in the missing numbers.

Set 1

	x	7	=	7
	x	7	=	28
	x	7	=	77
12	x	7	=	
	=	7	x	1
49	=		x	7
5	x	7	=	
	=	14	÷	7
	=	7	x	3
28	=	7	x	

Set 2

6	x	7	=	
	x	7	=	49
10	x	7	=	
	=	7	x	8
63	=	7	x	
	=	7	x	10
	=	7	x	11
	=	7	x	12
7	÷	7	=	
14	÷	7	=	

Set 3

35	÷	7	=	
5	=		÷	7
8	x	7	=	
	x	7	=	63
	=	42	÷	7
35	=	7	x	
10	=		÷	7
	=	77	÷	7
	÷	7	=	6
49	÷	7	=	

Set 4

4	=		÷	7
	=	49	÷	7
8	=		÷	7
	=	63	÷	7
84	÷	7	=	
1	=		÷	7
12	=		÷	7
	÷	7	=	11
	x	7	=	14
3	x	7	=	

Set 5

	x	7	=	56
9	x	7	=	
	=	42	÷	7
35	=	7	x	
10	=		÷	7
	=	77	÷	7
	÷	7	=	6
49	÷	7	=	
	÷	7	=	8
3	=		÷	7

Set 6

28	÷	7	=	
	÷	7	=	5
	=	35	÷	7
	x	7	=	56
9	x	7	=	
	=	42	÷	7
	=	7	x	5
	=	70	÷	7
11	=		÷	7
42	÷	7	=	

Set 7

14	÷	7	=	
	÷	7	=	3
70	=	7	x	
	=	7	x	11
7	x	7	=	
10	x	7	=	
56	=	7	x	
	=	7	x	9
	=	7	x	12
	÷	7	=	1

Set 8

11	=		÷	7
42	÷	7	=	
	÷	7	=	7
56	÷	7	=	
21	=	7	x	
	=	7	x	4
	x	7	=	42
7	x	7	=	
3	=		÷	7
4	=		÷	7

Set 9

	=	70	÷	7
11	=		÷	7
	÷	7	=	6
49	÷	7	=	
56	÷	7	=	
	=	21	÷	7
4	=		÷	7
42	=	7	x	
	÷	7	=	4
84	=	7	x	

1 Complete the maze by drawing a line through multiples of 7. Watch out for dead ends!

START HERE

14	35	67	42	68	22	99	65	45	74	24	34	77
7	22	35	49	63	44	85	24	78	23	24	33	57
14	22	44	7	32	45	4	78	1	6	8	35	70
28	35	42	84	49	27	7	25	77	24	64	25	86
56	64	24	64	56	77	70	90	75	23	66	24	76
63	24	12	65	63	34	22	35	86	35	77	32	35
19	64	49	42	14	64	45	28	24	32	56	87	46
33	24	88	86	7	28	70	77	63	56	27	32	24
79	68	54	35	77	35	76	23	75	14	21	56	65
97	34	23	89	33	77	99	32	24	79	28	3	25
42	24	68	24	26	64	35	32	56	88	49	21	**EXIT**

2 Fill in the gaps in the table.

a	7 + 7 + 7 + 7	4 x 7	28
b	7 + 7 + 7 + 7 + 7 + 7 + 7 + 7 + 7 + 7 + 7	11 x 7	
c			35
d	7 + 7 + 7 + 7 + 7 + 7 + 7 + 7 + 7 + 7		
e		1 x 7	
f	7 + 7 + 7 + 7 + 7 + 7		42
g			84
h	7 + 7 + 7 + 7 + 7 + 7 + 7 + 7 + 7		
i		3 x 7	
j	7 + 7 + 7 + 7 + 7 + 7 + 7		
k	7 + 7 + 7 + 7 + 7 + 7 + 7 + 7	8 x 7	
l			14

1 Calculate the area of each of these rectangles (not drawn to scale).

Example

7 cm

28 cm² | 4 cm

7 cm x 4 cm = 28 cm²

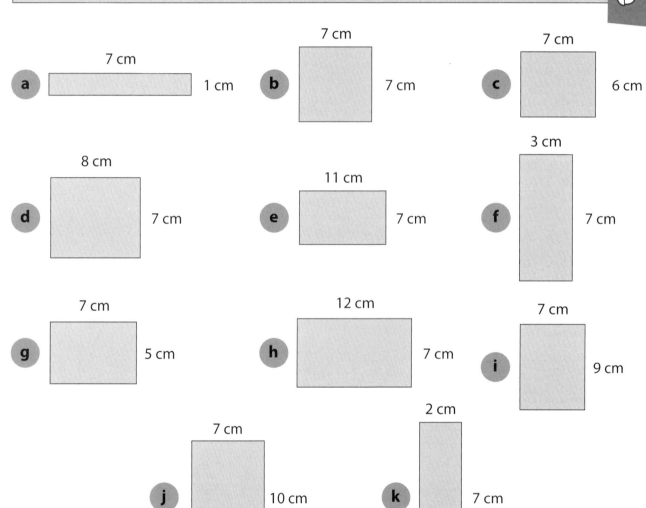

a 7 cm | 1 cm

b 7 cm | 7 cm

c 7 cm | 6 cm

d 8 cm | 7 cm

e 11 cm | 7 cm

f 3 cm | 7 cm

g 7 cm | 5 cm

h 12 cm | 7 cm

i 7 cm | 9 cm

j 7 cm | 10 cm

k 2 cm | 7 cm

2 Find the area of rectangles with these measurements.

a	50 cm long and 7 cm wide	
b	70 cm long and 12 cm wide	
c	7 cm long and 40 cm wide	

Ninja Challenge

1 Use the known multiplication facts to answer these questions.

Example

1 x 7 =	7
10 x 7 =	70
100 x 7 =	700

a

2 x 7 =	
20 x 7 =	
200 x 7 =	

b

3 x 7 =	
30 x 7 =	
300 x 7 =	

c

4 x 7 =	
40 x 7 =	
400 x 7 =	

d

5 x 7 =	
50 x 7 =	
500 x 7 =	

e

6 x 7 =	
60 x 7 =	
600 x 7 =	

f

7 x 7 =	
70 x 7 =	
700 x 7 =	

g

8 x 7 =	
80 x 7 =	
800 x 7 =	

h

9 x 7 =	
90 x 7 =	
900 x 7 =	

i

10 x 7 =	
100 x 7 =	
1,000 x 7 =	

j

11 x 7 =	
110 x 7 =	
1,100 x 7 =	

k

12 x 7 =	
120 x 7 =	
1,200 x 7 =	

2 Use the known multiplication facts to answer these questions.

Example

36 x 7	
30 x 7	210
6 x 7	42
Total:	252

a

28 x 7	
20 x 7	
8 x 7	
Total:	

b

75 x 7	
70 x 7	
5 x 7	
Total:	

c

39 x 7	
30 x 7	
9 x 7	
Total:	

d

57 x 7	
50 x 7	
7 x 7	
Total:	

e

48 x 7	
40 x 7	
8 x 7	
Total:	

f

284 x 7	
200 x 7	
80 x 7	
4 x 7	
Total:	

g

472 x 7	
400 x 7	
70 x 7	
2 x 7	
Total:	

h

395 x 7	
300 x 7	
90 x 7	
5 x 7	
Total:	

Complete these short division questions using the 7 times table.

You could write out the times table to help you with these questions.

1
```
7 | 1  7  9  2
```

2
```
7 | 1  1  4  1
```

3
```
7 | 1  3  7  2
```

4
```
7 | 1  8  5  5
```

5
```
7 | 2  2  7  5
```

6
```
7 | 9  9  4
```

7
```
7 | 1  0  1  5
```

8
```
7 | 2  0  8  6
```

9
```
7 | 4  6  0  6
```

10	2,492	÷	7	=
11	2,464	÷	7	=
12	2,023	÷	7	=
13	1,778	÷	7	=

14	3,808	÷	7	=
15	4,571	÷	7	=
16	3,738	÷	7	=
17	2,506	÷	7	=

Calculations

Use this space for jottings and written calculations.

$7 \times \div + -$

Write the multiplication or division calculation and answer for each of these word problems.

1	Oranges come in bags of 7. How many oranges will there be in 12 bags?	
2	Children are put into groups of 7. If there are 84 children, how many groups will there be?	
3	7 children share some marbles equally between them. If they get 7 marbles each, how many are there in total?	
4	There are 7 days in a week. How many days are there in 8 weeks?	
5	7 magazines are shared equally between 7 children. How many will they receive each?	
6	Mia has a biscuit every day. If she has 42 biscuits, how many weeks will they last for?	
7	Cakes are sold in packs of 7. Gemma needs 28 cakes for a party. How many packs will she need?	
8	Cushions have 7 stars stitched on them. How many stars will there be on 9 cushions?	
9	A machine produces a box every 7 minutes. How many boxes are produced after 35 minutes?	
10	A group of people are put into 7 teams. If there are 40 people in each team, how many people are there altogether?	
11	If a machine can produce 7 toys a minute, how many toys can be produced after 20 minutes?	
12	A group of 350 people sit at tables of 7. How many tables will they need so that everyone has a seat?	
13	A heptagon has 7 sides. How many sides are there in 80 heptagons?	
14	A tin of baked beans contains 400 beans. How many beans will there be in 7 tins?	

8

Use the 7 times table to find these equivalent fractions.

Example

$\xrightarrow{\div 7}$ $\xrightarrow{\times 7}$

$\dfrac{7}{35} = \dfrac{1}{5}$ $\dfrac{1}{5} = \dfrac{7}{35}$

$\xleftarrow{\div 7}$ $\xleftarrow{\times 7}$

Multiply or divide the numerator and the denominator by the same number.

1 $\dfrac{2}{3} = \dfrac{14}{\boxed{}}$

2 $\dfrac{49}{56} = \dfrac{\boxed{}}{8}$

3 $\dfrac{3}{5} = \dfrac{\boxed{}}{35}$

4 $\dfrac{77}{84} = \dfrac{11}{\boxed{}}$

5 $\dfrac{10}{11} = \dfrac{\boxed{}}{77}$

6 $\dfrac{28}{35} = \dfrac{4}{\boxed{}}$

7 $\dfrac{14}{56} = \dfrac{2}{\boxed{}}$

8 $\dfrac{4}{12} = \dfrac{\boxed{}}{84}$

9 $\dfrac{3}{11} = \dfrac{21}{\boxed{}}$

10 $\dfrac{7}{\boxed{}} = \dfrac{1}{6}$

11 $\dfrac{\boxed{}}{28} = \dfrac{1}{4}$

12 $\dfrac{1}{7} = \dfrac{7}{\boxed{}}$

13 $\dfrac{5}{11} = \dfrac{\boxed{}}{77}$

14 $\dfrac{\boxed{}}{56} = \dfrac{5}{8}$

15 $\dfrac{7}{35} = \dfrac{\boxed{}}{5}$

16 $\dfrac{3}{11} = \dfrac{21}{\boxed{}}$

17 $\dfrac{11}{12} = \dfrac{\boxed{}}{84}$

18 $\dfrac{4}{7} = \dfrac{28}{\boxed{}}$

19 $\dfrac{8}{11} = \dfrac{56}{\boxed{}}$

20 $\dfrac{\boxed{}}{42} = \dfrac{5}{6}$

21 $\dfrac{\boxed{}}{77} = \dfrac{10}{11}$

22 $\dfrac{5}{9} = \dfrac{35}{\boxed{}}$

Use the given fraction to find the whole number.

Example

$\frac{1}{7}$ of | 56 | is 8

| 8 | 8 | 8 | 8 | 8 | 8 | 8 |
| 56 |

1 $\frac{1}{7}$ of ☐ is 7

| 7 | | | | | | |

2 $\frac{1}{7}$ of ☐ is 4

| 4 | | | | | | |

3 $\frac{1}{7}$ of ☐ is 3

| 3 | | | | | | |

4 $\frac{1}{7}$ of ☐ is 11

| 11 | | | | | | |

5 $\frac{1}{7}$ of ☐ is 10

| 10 | | | | | | |

6 $\frac{1}{7}$ of ☐ is 12

| 12 | | | | | | |

7 $\frac{1}{7}$ of ☐ is 9

| 9 | | | | | | |

8 $\frac{1}{7}$ of ☐ is 6

| 6 | | | | | | |

9 $\frac{1}{7}$ of ☐ is 2

10 $\frac{1}{7}$ of ☐ is 5

11 $\frac{1}{7}$ of ☐ is 25

12 $\frac{1}{7}$ of ☐ is 20

13 $\frac{1}{7}$ of ☐ is 50

14 $\frac{1}{7}$ of ☐ is 15

15 $\frac{1}{7}$ of ☐ is 30

16 $\frac{1}{7}$ of ☐ is 60

17 $\frac{1}{7}$ of ☐ is 40

18 $\frac{1}{7}$ of ☐ is 90

Find $\frac{1}{7}$ of the numbers below by dividing them by 7.

Example

$\frac{1}{7}$ of 21 = [3]

3	3	3	3	3	3	3

21

1 $\frac{1}{7}$ of 56 = [ ]

2 $\frac{1}{7}$ of 14 = [ ]

3 $\frac{1}{7}$ of 42 = [ ]

4 $\frac{1}{7}$ of 70 = [ ]

5 $\frac{1}{7}$ of 28 = [ ]

6 $\frac{1}{7}$ of 77 = [ ]

7 $\frac{1}{7}$ of 35 = [ ]

8 $\frac{1}{7}$ of 84 = [ ]

9 $\frac{1}{7}$ of 7 = [ ]

10 $\frac{1}{7}$ of 49 = [ ]

11 $\frac{1}{7}$ of 63 = [ ]

12 $\frac{1}{7}$ of 770 = [ ]

13 $\frac{1}{7}$ of 140 = [ ]

14 $\frac{1}{7}$ of 700 = [ ]

15 $\frac{1}{7}$ of 91 = [ ]

16 $\frac{1}{7}$ of 210 = [ ]

17 $\frac{1}{7}$ of 490 = [ ]

18 $\frac{1}{7}$ of 350 = [ ]

7 TIMES TABLE

Adjust these ingredients lists by the amounts shown. Use the number facts if you need to.

Example

Pancake recipe	
1 person	**7 people**
100 g plain flour	700 g plain flour
2 large eggs	14 large eggs
300 ml milk	2,100 ml milk

x 7

Multiply or divide each ingredient by the same number to scale the recipe up or down.

1

Milkshake recipe	
2 people	**14 people**
200 ml milk	
3 bananas	
2 chocolate bars	

x 7

2

Flapjack recipe	
1 flapjack traybake	**7 flapjack traybakes**
200 g oats	
120 g butter	
110 g brown sugar	

x 7

3

Fudge recipe	
35 pieces	**5 pieces**
420 g sugar	
490 ml cream	
350 g butter	

÷ 7

4

Rock cakes recipe	
21 rock cakes	**3 rock cakes**
210 g flour	
77 g sugar	
140 g butter	
70 g dried fruit	

÷ 7

5

Smoothie recipe	
1 smoothie	**7 smoothies**
11 strawberries	
9 cherries	
50 ml yoghurt	
100 ml juice	

x 7

Calculations

Use this space for jottings and written calculations.

Find the perimeters of these regular polygons (not drawn to scale).

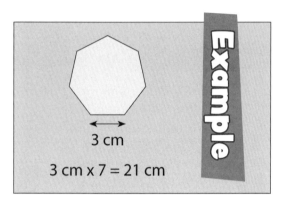

Example

3 cm

3 cm x 7 = 21 cm

Multiply the length of one side by the number of sides to find the perimeter of regular polygons.

1
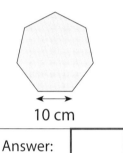
10 cm

Answer:

2
12 cm

Answer:

3
4 cm

Answer:

4
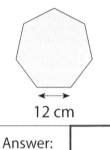
11 cm

Answer:

5
8 cm

Answer:

6
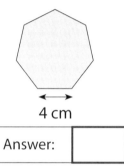
9 cm

Answer:

7
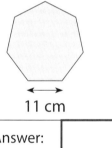
7 cm

Answer:

8
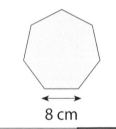
7 cm

Answer:

9
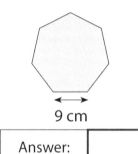
7 cm

Answer:

10

70 cm

Answer:

11
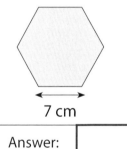
70 cm

Answer:

12
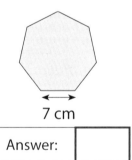
70 cm

Answer:

8 TIMES TABLE

Can you see any patterns in the 8 times table?

1 **Shade in or circle the multiples of 8 up to 100.**

1	2	3	4	5	6	7	8	9	10
11	12	13	14	15	16	17	18	19	20
21	22	23	24	25	26	27	28	29	30
31	32	33	34	35	36	37	38	39	40
41	42	43	44	45	46	47	48	49	50
51	52	53	54	55	56	57	58	59	60
61	62	63	64	65	66	67	68	69	70
71	72	73	74	75	76	77	78	79	80
81	82	83	84	85	86	87	88	89	90
91	92	93	94	95	96	97	98	99	100

2 **Find and circle the 8 times table in this number search.**

1	x	8	=	8	x	4	x	8	=	12	32	4
48	12	x	8	=	88	5	x	8	=	x	8	x
11	3	8	=	8	7	48	56	72	64	8	80	8
96	x	8	x	5	x	8	=	40	16	=	6	=
8	8	8	16	8	8	x	16	9	32	96	x	32
56	=	64	=	24	=	40	40	x	9	6	8	6
2	32	72	8	88	56	64	88	8	x	x	=	x
3	x	8	=	24	80	64	88	=	8	8	48	8
8	x	8	5	x	8	=	48	80	=	=	32	=
16	24	x	=	4	x	8	=	44	72	96	=	88
3	x	8	=	16	10	x	8	=	80	8	8	24

Fill in the missing numbers.

Set 1

1	x	8	=	
	x	8	=	16
	÷	8	=	10
88	÷	8	=	
	÷	8	=	12
1	=		÷	8
9	=		÷	8
	=	80	÷	8
11	=		÷	8
48	=		x	8

Set 2

	=	7	x	8
16	÷	8	=	
24	÷	8	=	
	x	8	=	64
	=	3	x	8
32	=		x	8
32	÷	8	=	
56	÷	8	=	
	÷	8	=	8
2	=		÷	8

Set 3

	=	24	÷	8
	=	8	x	8
	=	9	x	8
80	=		x	8
72	÷	8	=	
4	=		÷	8
5	=		÷	8
	=	11	x	8
96	=		x	8
8	÷	8	=	

Set 4

12	=		÷	8
	x	8	=	72
	x	8	=	80
11	x	8	=	
4	x	8	=	
	x	8	=	40
	x	8	=	56
12	x	8	=	
8	=		x	8
16	=		X	8

Set 5

	=	1	x	8
	=	2	x	8
	x	8	=	24
	=	5	x	8
8	=		÷	8
	x	8	=	48
	=	48	÷	8
7	=		÷	8
40	÷	8	=	
	÷	8	=	6

Set 6

5	=		÷	8
	=	11	x	8
96	=		x	8
8	÷	8	=	
	=	96	÷	8
	x	8	=	72
10	x	8	=	
	x	8	=	88
4	x	8	=	
5	x	8	=	

Set 7

24	÷	8	=	
	x	8	=	64
	=	3	x	8
32	=		x	8
	÷	8	=	4
	÷	8	=	7
64	÷	8	=	
	=	16	÷	8
	=	24	÷	8
64	=		x	8

Set 8

	=	2	x	8
	x	8	=	24
	÷	8	=	3
8	x	8	=	
	=	3	x	8
32	=		x	8
	÷	8	=	4
40	=		x	8
8	=		÷	8
	x	8	=	48

Set 9

	=	96	÷	8
	x	8	=	72
10	x	8	=	
	÷	8	=	2
	÷	8	=	3
8	x	8	=	
	=	3	x	8
32	=		x	8
11	x	8	=	
4	x	8	=	

1 **Complete the maze by drawing a line through multiples of 8. Watch out for dead ends!**

START HERE

8	48	16	40	96	88	64	56	37	52	47	24	28
53	24	40	53	65	57	72	45	79	48	42	23	64
35	23	48	67	36	16	80	11	22	56	36	36	35
31	57	43	89	32	38	88	16	24	32	53	45	23
35	16	76	99	34	35	72	34	36	56	64	13	53
75	71	35	8	12	44	10	23	35	54	72	80	56
35	6	56	4	8	32	43	68	57	21	80	55	42
90	3	53	48	19	78	50	65	64	37	8	35	53
43	6	7	24	64	48	40	64	16	32	16	26	32
78	40	24	46	79	43	46	70	72	26	25	32	25
88	22	62	32	34	35	43	45	96	80	88	16	**EXIT**

2 **Fill in the gaps in the table.**

a	8 + 8 + 8 + 8	4 x 8	32
b	8	1 x 8	
c			80
d	8 + 8 + 8 + 8 + 8 + 8 + 8 + 8 + 8 + 8 + 8 + 8		
e	8 + 8 + 8 + 8 + 8		40
f		11 x 8	
g			56
h	8 + 8 + 8 + 8 + 8 + 8 + 8 + 8		
i	8 + 8 + 8		24
j			72
k	8 + 8	2 x 8	
l	8 + 8 + 8 + 8 + 8 + 8		48

1 Calculate the area of each of these rectangles (not drawn to scale).

8 cm

16 cm²   2 cm   8 cm x 2 cm = 16 cm²

a 8 cm — 1 cm

b  8 cm — 9 cm

c 10 cm — 8 cm

d 8 cm — 11 cm

e  6 cm — 8 cm

f 3 cm — 8 cm

g 8 cm — 8 cm

h 2 cm — 8 cm

i  8 cm — 12 cm

j 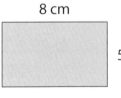 8 cm — 4 cm

k 8 cm — 5 cm

2 Find the area of rectangles with these measurements.

a	50 cm long and 8 cm wide	
b	80 cm long and 12 cm wide	
c	8 cm long and 40 cm wide	

Ninja Challenge

1 **Use the known multiplication facts to answer these questions.**

Example	
1 x 8 =	8
10 x 8 =	80
100 x 8 =	800

a
2 x 8 =	
20 x 8 =	
200 x 8 =	

b
3 x 8 =	
30 x 8 =	
300 x 8 =	

c
4 x 8 =	
40 x 8 =	
400 x 8 =	

d
5 x 8 =	
50 x 8 =	
500 x 8 =	

e
6 x 8 =	
60 x 8 =	
600 x 8 =	

f
7 x 8 =	
70 x 8 =	
700 x 8 =	

g
8 x 8 =	
80 x 8 =	
800 x 8 =	

h
9 x 8 =	
90 x 8 =	
900 x 8 =	

i
10 x 8 =	
100 x 8 =	
1,000 x 8 =	

j
11 x 8 =	
110 x 8 =	
1,100 x 8 =	

k
12 x 8 =	
120 x 8 =	
1,200 x 8 =	

2 **Use the known multiplication facts to answer these questions.**

Example 36 x 8	
30 x 8	240
6 x 8	48
Total:	288

a
28 x 8	
20 x 8	
8 x 8	
Total:	

b
75 x 8	
70 x 8	
5 x 8	
Total:	

c
39 x 8	
30 x 8	
9 x 8	
Total:	

d
57 x 8	
50 x 8	
7 x 8	
Total:	

e
48 x 8	
40 x 8	
8 x 8	
Total:	

f
284 x 8	
200 x 8	
80 x 8	
4 x 8	
Total:	

g
472 x 8	
400 x 8	
70 x 8	
2 x 8	
Total:	

h
395 x 8	
300 x 8	
90 x 8	
5 x 8	
Total:	

6

Complete these short division questions using the 8 times table.

Example

$968 \div 8 = 121$

$$
\begin{array}{c|ccc}
 & 1 & 2 & 1 \\
\hline
8 & 9 & {}^{1}6 & 8 \\
\end{array}
$$

> You could write out the times table to help you with these questions.

1

$$
\begin{array}{c|ccc}
8 & 3 & 2 & 8 \\
\end{array}
$$

2

$$
\begin{array}{c|cccc}
8 & 1 & 8 & 8 & 0 \\
\end{array}
$$

3

$$
\begin{array}{c|ccc}
8 & 7 & 8 & 4 \\
\end{array}
$$

4

$$
\begin{array}{c|ccc}
8 & 6 & 0 & 8 \\
\end{array}
$$

5

$$
\begin{array}{c|ccc}
8 & 6 & 0 & 0 \\
\end{array}
$$

6

$$
\begin{array}{c|cccc}
8 & 1 & 2 & 2 & 4 \\
\end{array}
$$

7

$$
\begin{array}{c|cccc}
8 & 1 & 1 & 6 & 0 \\
\end{array}
$$

8

$$
\begin{array}{c|cccc}
8 & 2 & 6 & 0 & 0 \\
\end{array}
$$

9

$$
\begin{array}{c|cccc}
7 & 2 & 0 & 0 & 8 \\
\end{array}
$$

10	680	÷	8	=
11	1,336	÷	8	=
12	2,024	÷	8	=
13	1,232	÷	8	=

14	1,888	÷	8	=
15	1,392	÷	8	=
16	1,808	÷	8	=
17	6,768	÷	8	=

Calculations

Use this space for jottings and written calculations.

8 TIMES TABLE

Write the multiplication or division calculation and answer for each of these word problems.

1	1 octopus has 8 legs. How many will 12 have?	
2	Bottles of water come in packs of 8. A teacher needs to buy enough water for 48 children. How many packs will he need to buy?	
3	A bucket contains 56 litres of water. If it is shared equally into 8 smaller buckets, how much water will be in each smaller bucket?	
4	There are 8 pairs of shoes on a rack. How many shoes are there in total?	
5	8 children share £72 equally between themselves. How much will they have each?	
6	A chocolate bar is made up of 8 squares. How many squares will there be in 11 bars of chocolate?	
7	Packets of crisps are sold in bags of 8. How many packets will there be in 5 bags?	
8	A shelf holds 8 books. How many shelves will be needed for 96 books?	
9	8 sheets of paper are shared equally between 8 children. How many sheets of paper will each child get?	
10	A pack of paper contains 480 sheets. If they are shared equally into 8 smaller packs, how many sheets of paper will be in each pack?	
11	A classroom has 240 books, which are put into boxes of 8. How many boxes will be needed in total?	
12	1 spider has 8 legs. How many legs will 200 spiders have?	
13	A pack of pencils is shared equally between 8 classes. If each class receives 30 pencils, how many were there in the pack?	
14	Tables in a café seat 8 people. If there are 20 tables, how many people can be seated in total?	

8

Use the 8 times table to find these equivalent fractions.

Example

$$\frac{8}{40} = \frac{1}{5}$$ ÷ 8 ÷ 8

$$\frac{1}{5} = \frac{8}{40}$$ x 8 x 8

Multiply or divide the numerator and the denominator by the same number.

1 $\dfrac{3}{5} = \dfrac{24}{\boxed{}}$

2 $\dfrac{1}{4} = \dfrac{\boxed{}}{32}$

3 $\dfrac{72}{96} = \dfrac{9}{\boxed{}}$

4 $\dfrac{40}{\boxed{}} = \dfrac{5}{10}$

5 $\dfrac{\boxed{}}{8} = \dfrac{56}{64}$

6 $\dfrac{80}{88} = \dfrac{10}{\boxed{}}$

7 $\dfrac{5}{6} = \dfrac{\boxed{}}{48}$

8 $\dfrac{\boxed{}}{40} = \dfrac{3}{5}$

9 $\dfrac{4}{\boxed{}} = \dfrac{32}{88}$

10 $\dfrac{8}{72} = \dfrac{\boxed{}}{9}$

11 $\dfrac{32}{72} = \dfrac{4}{\boxed{}}$

12 $\dfrac{2}{6} = \dfrac{\boxed{}}{48}$

13 $\dfrac{9}{\boxed{}} = \dfrac{72}{88}$

14 $\dfrac{7}{10} = \dfrac{\boxed{}}{80}$

15 $\dfrac{\boxed{}}{88} = \dfrac{5}{11}$

16 $\dfrac{6}{11} = \dfrac{48}{\boxed{}}$

17 $\dfrac{\boxed{}}{12} = \dfrac{88}{96}$

18 $\dfrac{4}{7} = \dfrac{32}{\boxed{}}$

19 $\dfrac{8}{11} = \dfrac{\boxed{}}{88}$

20 $\dfrac{40}{48} = \dfrac{\boxed{}}{6}$

21 $\dfrac{80}{96} = \dfrac{10}{\boxed{}}$

22 $\dfrac{5}{9} = \dfrac{40}{\boxed{}}$

Times Tables Ninja © Sarah Farrell, 2022

Use the given fraction to find the whole number.

Example

$\frac{1}{8}$ of ☐56☐ is 7

7	7	7	7	7	7	7	7

56

1 $\frac{1}{8}$ of ☐ is 4

4							

2 $\frac{1}{8}$ of ☐ is 8

8							

3 $\frac{1}{8}$ of ☐ is 3

3							

4 $\frac{1}{8}$ of ☐ is 11

11							

5 $\frac{1}{8}$ of ☐ is 10

10							

6 $\frac{1}{8}$ of ☐ is 12

12							

7 $\frac{1}{8}$ of ☐ is 9

9							

8 $\frac{1}{8}$ of ☐ is 6

6							

9 $\frac{1}{8}$ of ☐ is 2

10 $\frac{1}{8}$ of ☐ is 5

11 $\frac{1}{8}$ of ☐ is 25

12 $\frac{1}{8}$ of ☐ is 20

13 $\frac{1}{8}$ of ☐ is 50

14 $\frac{1}{8}$ of ☐ is 15

15 $\frac{1}{8}$ of ☐ is 30

16 $\frac{1}{8}$ of ☐ is 60

17 $\frac{1}{8}$ of ☐ is 100

18 $\frac{1}{8}$ of ☐ is 110

Find $\frac{1}{8}$ of the numbers below by dividing them by 8.

Example

$\frac{1}{8}$ of 24 = 3

3	3	3	3	3	3	3	3
24							

1 $\frac{1}{8}$ of 64 =

2 $\frac{1}{8}$ of 8 =

3 $\frac{1}{8}$ of 32 =

4 $\frac{1}{8}$ of 48 =

5 $\frac{1}{8}$ of 72 =

6 $\frac{1}{8}$ of 16 =

7 $\frac{1}{8}$ of 56 =

8 $\frac{1}{8}$ of 88 =

9 $\frac{1}{8}$ of 80 =

10 $\frac{1}{8}$ of 40 =

11 $\frac{1}{8}$ of 96 =

12 $\frac{1}{8}$ of 480 =

13 $\frac{1}{8}$ of 800 =

14 $\frac{1}{8}$ of 320 =

15 $\frac{1}{8}$ of 400 =

16 $\frac{1}{8}$ of 880 =

17 $\frac{1}{8}$ of 160 =

18 $\frac{1}{8}$ of 8,000 =

Adjust these ingredients lists by the amounts shown. Use the number facts if you need to.

Example

Pancake recipe	
1 person	**8 people**
100 g plain flour	800 g plain flour
2 large eggs	16 large eggs
300 ml milk	2,400 ml milk

x 8

Multiply or divide each ingredient by the same number to scale the recipe up or down.

1

Milkshake recipe	
2 people	**16 people**
200 ml milk	
3 bananas	
2 chocolate bars	

x 8

2

Flapjack recipe	
1 flapjack traybake	**8 flapjack traybakes**
200 g oats	
120 g butter	
110 g brown sugar	

x 8

3

Fudge recipe	
40 pieces	**5 pieces**
480 g sugar	
400 ml cream	
56 g butter	

÷ 8

4

Rock cakes recipe	
24 rock cakes	**3 rock cakes**
240 g flour	
72 g sugar	
160 g butter	
96 g dried fruit	

÷ 8

5

Smoothie recipe	
1 smoothie	**8 smoothies**
11 strawberries	
9 cherries	
50 ml yoghurt	
100 ml juice	

x 8

Calculations

Use this space for jottings and written calculations.

12

Find the perimeters of these regular polygons (not drawn to scale).

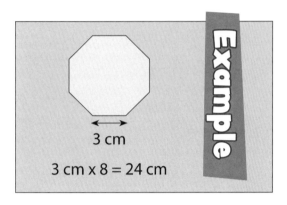

Example

3 cm

3 cm x 8 = 24 cm

Multiply the length of one side by the number of sides to find the perimeter of regular polygons.

1

10 cm

Answer:

2

12 cm

Answer:

3

4 cm

Answer:

4
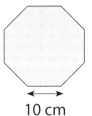

11 cm

Answer:

5
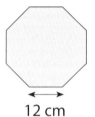

8 cm

Answer:

6
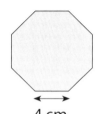

9 cm

Answer:

7
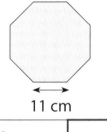

8 cm

Answer:

8

8 cm

Answer:

9

8 cm

Answer:

10
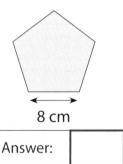

80 cm

Answer:

11
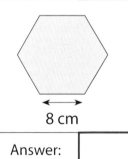

80 cm

Answer:

12
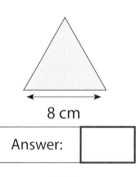

80 cm

Answer:

Can you see any patterns in the 9 times table?

1 Shade in or circle the multiples of 9 up to 100.

1	2	3	4	5	6	7	8	9	10
11	12	13	14	15	16	17	18	19	20
21	22	23	24	25	26	27	28	29	30
31	32	33	34	35	36	37	38	39	40
41	42	43	44	45	46	47	48	49	50
51	52	53	54	55	56	57	58	59	60
61	62	63	64	65	66	67	68	69	70
71	72	73	74	75	76	77	78	79	80
81	82	83	84	85	86	87	88	89	90
91	92	93	94	95	96	97	98	99	100

2 Find and circle the 9 times table in this number search.

1	x	9	=	9	4	72	36	12	x	9	=	108
5	10	9	x	4	x	27	2	x	9	=	81	9
11	x	9	=	99	9	7	=	x	81	11	45	8
6	9	7	x	9	=	90	x	4	9	3	99	x
x	=	3	63	6	54	72	x	9	x	=	10	9
9	90	6	4	5	x	9	=	45	=	9	18	=
=	4	1	x	x	90	9	3	90	12	63	90	72
45	81	54	9	54	72	8	=	x	2	x	36	x
3	x	9	=	27	x	18	36	54	9	45	108	63
108	7	9	36	x	27	11	x	9	=	90	9	=
4	x	9	=	81	=	99	9	x	9	=	81	18

9 TIMES TABLE 2

Fill in the missing numbers.

Set 1

1	x	9	=	
5	=		÷	9
	÷	9	=	11
	x	9	=	27
4	x	9	=	
	x	9	=	90
11	x	9	=	
63	÷	9	=	
	÷	9	=	8
36	=		x	9

Set 2

	÷	9	=	6
7	=		÷	9
8	=		÷	9
	x	9	=	63
8	x	9	=	
	=	7	x	9
72	=		x	9
	x	9	=	45
	x	9	=	54
81	=		x	9

Set 3

90	=		x	9
99	=		x	9
	=	12	x	9
	÷	9	=	4
45	÷	9	=	
9	÷	9	=	
	x	9	=	81
	=	5	x	9
54	=		x	9
18	÷	9	=	

Set 4

	÷	9	=	3
2	=		÷	9
	÷	9	=	12
1	=		÷	9
	x	9	=	108
9	=		x	9
6	=		÷	9
	=	81	÷	9
	÷	9	=	9
90	÷	9	=	

Set 5

	÷	9	=	9
90	÷	9	=	
18	=		x	9
	=	3	x	9
10	=		÷	9
2	x	9	=	
	=	27	÷	9
4	=		÷	9
	=	99	÷	9
12	=		÷	9

Set 6

2	=		÷	9
	÷	9	=	12
1	=		÷	9
12	x	9	=	
9	=		x	9
	=	54	÷	9
9	=		÷	9
81	÷	9	=	
	÷	9	=	10
	=	2	x	9

Set 7

	=	5	x	9
54	=		x	9
	÷	9	=	2
8	=		÷	9
7	x	9	=	
	x	9	=	72
63	=		x	9
	=	8	x	9
	÷	9	=	3
2	=		÷	9

Set 8

99	=		x	9
	=	12	x	9
36	÷	9	=	
	÷	9	=	5
	÷	9	=	1
	x	9	=	81
	=	5	x	9
54	=		x	9
	÷	9	=	2
	÷	9	=	3

Set 9

	÷	9	=	8
36	=		x	9
54	÷	9	=	
	=	63	÷	9
	=	72	÷	9
	÷	9	=	12
	=	9	÷	9
	x	9	=	108
9	=		x	9
6	=		÷	9

Times Tables Ninja © Sarah Farrell, 2022

1 Complete the maze by drawing a line through multiples of 9. Watch out for dead ends!

START HERE

18	45	78	42	77	99	44	57	87	32	12	77	89
27	32	56	86	22	55	77	6	2	14	5	75	63
54	33	89	32	57	88	14	8	18	63	11	34	88
45	23	68	56	78	96	33	36	27	89	12	18	81
108	24	53	23	6	53	19	7	36	32	65	36	72
63	90	99	45	54	27	63	9	90	99	63	27	18
72	53	19	81	29	89	39	49	59	90	22	11	27
45	67	75	72	52	65	85	107	65	72	19	54	108
63	42	34	90	90	42	36	75	42	90	32	37	99
9	78	86	108	68	68	104	108	53	24	99	65	90
65	25	47	4	53	9	75	36	90	53	24	97	**EXIT**

2 Fill in the gaps in the table.

a	9 + 9 + 9	3 x 9	27
b	9 + 9 + 9 + 9 + 9 + 9 + 9 + 9	8 x 9	
c		2 x 9	18
d	9 + 9 + 9 + 9 + 9 + 9 + 9		
e			99
f	9		9
g			108
h	9 + 9 + 9 + 9 + 9 + 9 + 9 + 9 + 9 + 9		
i		6 x 9	
j			81
k	9 + 9 + 9 + 9 + 9		
l	9 + 9 + 9 + 9		36

1 **Calculate the area of each of these rectangles (not drawn to scale).**

Example

9 cm

18 cm² · 2 cm · 9 cm x 2 cm = 18 cm²

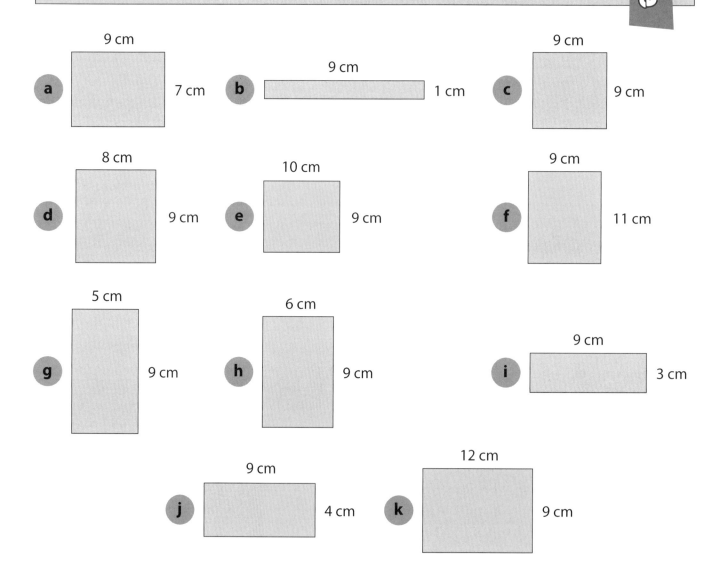

a 9 cm / 7 cm

b 9 cm / 1 cm

c 9 cm / 9 cm

d 8 cm / 9 cm

e 10 cm / 9 cm

f 9 cm / 11 cm

g 5 cm / 9 cm

h 6 cm / 9 cm

i 9 cm / 3 cm

j 9 cm / 4 cm

k 12 cm / 9 cm

2 **Find the area of rectangles with these measurements.**

Ninja Challenge

a	50 cm long and 9 cm wide	
b	90 cm long and 12 cm wide	
c	9 cm long and 40 cm wide	

1 Use the known multiplication facts to answer these questions.

Example		
1 x 9 =	9
10 x 9 =	90
100 x 9 =	900

a

2 x 9 =	
20 x 9 =	
200 x 9 =	

b

3 x 9 =	
30 x 9 =	
300 x 9 =	

c

4 x 9 =	
40 x 9 =	
400 x 9 =	

d

5 x 9 =	
50 x 9 =	
500 x 9 =	

e

6 x 9 =	
60 x 9 =	
600 x 9 =	

f

7 x 9 =	
70 x 9 =	
700 x 9 =	

g

8 x 9 =	
80 x 9 =	
800 x 9 =	

h

9 x 9 =	
90 x 9 =	
900 x 9 =	

i

10 x 9 =	
100 x 9 =	
1,000 x 9 =	

j

11 x 9 =	
110 x 9 =	
1,100 x 9 =	

k

12 x 9 =	
120 x 9 =	
1,200 x 9 =	

2 Use the known multiplication facts to answer these questions.

Example — 36 x 9

30 x 9	270
6 x 9	54
Total:	324

a — 28 x 9

20 x 9	
8 x 9	
Total:	

b — 75 x 9

70 x 9	
5 x 9	
Total:	

c — 39 x 9

30 x 9	
9 x 9	
Total:	

d — 57 x 9

50 x 9	
7 x 9	
Total:	

e — 48 x 9

40 x 9	
8 x 9	
Total:	

f — 284 x 9

200 x 9	
80 x 9	
4 x 9	
Total:	

g — 472 x 9

400 x 9	
70 x 9	
2 x 9	
Total:	

h — 395 x 9

300 x 9	
90 x 9	
5 x 9	
Total:	

6

Complete these short division questions using the 9 times table.

$882 \div 9 = 98$

```
        0    9    8
   ┌─────────────────
 9 │  8   ⁸8   ⁷2
```

You could write out the times table to help you with these questions.

1
```
9 │ 1   1   0   7
```

2
```
9 │ 2   8   9   8
```

3
```
9 │ 7   7   4
```

4
```
9 │ 6   8   4
```

5
```
9 │ 6   2   1
```

6
```
9 │ 2   2   0   5
```

7
```
9 │ 1   4   8   5
```

8
```
9 │ 9   7   2
```

9
```
9 │ 5   0   6   7
```

10	4,707	÷	9	=
11	1,413	÷	9	=
12	4,365	÷	9	=
13	6,678	÷	9	=

14	5,967	÷	9	=
15	2,385	÷	9	=
16	2,412	÷	9	=
17	5,868	÷	9	=

Calculations

Use this space for jottings and written calculations.

Times Tables Ninja © Sarah Farrell, 2022

Write the multiplication or division calculation and answer for each of these word problems.

1	9 children each have 7 books. How many books are there altogether?	
2	A small bag of sweets weighs 108 g. The sweets are shared equally between 9 children. How many grams will they get each?	
3	There are 27 children in a class. They get into groups of 9. How many groups will there be?	
4	A cat has 9 kittens. Each kitten eats 8 biscuits. How many biscuits do they eat in total?	
5	99 stones are shared equally into 9 piles. How many stones are there in each pile?	
6	A type of butterfly has 9 spots on each wing. How many spots will one butterfly have in total?	
7	A machine makes 9 boxes every 10 minutes. How many will it make in an hour?	
8	A child reads for 9 minutes a day. How many minutes will he read for in a week?	
9	A pile of 90 books is shared equally between 9 children. How many will they get each?	
10	Snacks come in bags of 9. If there are 50 bags, how many snacks will there be?	
11	A pile of balls is separated into 9 equal groups. If there are 90 balls in each group, how many balls are there in total?	
12	9 children each read 120 pages of their books. How many pages have been read altogether?	
13	A school shirt has 9 buttons. If there are 30 school shirts, how many buttons are there in total?	
14	A pencil pot holds 9 pencils. If there are 180 pencils, how many pots will be needed to hold them all?	

8

Use the 9 times table to find these equivalent fractions.

Multiply or divide the numerator and the denominator by the same number.

1 $\dfrac{2}{3} = \dfrac{18}{\Box}$

2 $\dfrac{63}{72} = \dfrac{\Box}{8}$

3 $\dfrac{3}{\Box} = \dfrac{27}{45}$

4 $\dfrac{\Box}{108} = \dfrac{11}{12}$

5 $\dfrac{10}{11} = \dfrac{\Box}{99}$

6 $\dfrac{36}{45} = \dfrac{4}{\Box}$

7 $\dfrac{18}{72} = \dfrac{\Box}{8}$

8 $\dfrac{4}{12} = \dfrac{36}{\Box}$

9 $\dfrac{\Box}{11} = \dfrac{27}{99}$

10 $\dfrac{9}{54} = \dfrac{\Box}{6}$

11 $\dfrac{9}{\Box} = \dfrac{1}{4}$

12 $\dfrac{1}{7} = \dfrac{\Box}{63}$

13 $\dfrac{\Box}{11} = \dfrac{45}{99}$

14 $\dfrac{45}{72} = \dfrac{5}{\Box}$

15 $\dfrac{9}{45} = \dfrac{1}{\Box}$

16 $\dfrac{3}{11} = \dfrac{\Box}{99}$

17 $\dfrac{11}{\Box} = \dfrac{99}{108}$

18 $\dfrac{4}{7} = \dfrac{\Box}{63}$

19 $\dfrac{8}{11} = \dfrac{72}{\Box}$

20 $\dfrac{45}{54} = \dfrac{\Box}{6}$

21 $\dfrac{\Box}{99} = \dfrac{10}{11}$

22 $\dfrac{5}{9} = \dfrac{45}{\Box}$

Use the given fraction to find the whole number.

Example

$\dfrac{1}{9}$ of $\boxed{72}$ is 8

8	8	8	8	8	8	8	8	8
				72				

1 $\dfrac{1}{9}$ of $\boxed{}$ is 7

7								

2 $\dfrac{1}{9}$ of $\boxed{}$ is 4

4								

3 $\dfrac{1}{9}$ of $\boxed{}$ is 3

3								

4 $\dfrac{1}{9}$ of $\boxed{}$ is 11

11								

5 $\dfrac{1}{9}$ of $\boxed{}$ is 10

10								

6 $\dfrac{1}{9}$ of $\boxed{}$ is 12

12								

7 $\dfrac{1}{9}$ of $\boxed{}$ is 9

9								

8 $\dfrac{1}{9}$ of $\boxed{}$ is 6

6								

9 $\dfrac{1}{9}$ of $\boxed{}$ is 2

10 $\dfrac{1}{9}$ of $\boxed{}$ is 5

11 $\dfrac{1}{9}$ of $\boxed{}$ is 25

12 $\dfrac{1}{9}$ of $\boxed{}$ is 20

13 $\dfrac{1}{9}$ of $\boxed{}$ is 50

14 $\dfrac{1}{9}$ of $\boxed{}$ is 15

15 $\dfrac{1}{9}$ of $\boxed{}$ is 30

16 $\dfrac{1}{9}$ of $\boxed{}$ is 60

17 $\dfrac{1}{9}$ of $\boxed{}$ is 70

18 $\dfrac{1}{9}$ of $\boxed{}$ is 40

Find $\frac{1}{9}$ of the numbers below by dividing them by 9.

Example

$\frac{1}{9}$ of 27 = $\boxed{3}$

3	3	3	3	3	3	3	3	3
				27				

1 $\frac{1}{9}$ of 81 = ☐

2 $\frac{1}{9}$ of 9 = ☐

3 $\frac{1}{9}$ of 54 = ☐

4 $\frac{1}{9}$ of 72 = ☐

5 $\frac{1}{9}$ of 36 = ☐

6 $\frac{1}{9}$ of 18 = ☐

7 $\frac{1}{9}$ of 90 = ☐

8 $\frac{1}{9}$ of 45 = ☐

9 $\frac{1}{9}$ of 108 = ☐

10 $\frac{1}{9}$ of 63 = ☐

11 $\frac{1}{9}$ of 99 = ☐

12 $\frac{1}{9}$ of 180 = ☐

13 $\frac{1}{9}$ of 990 = ☐

14 $\frac{1}{9}$ of 450 = ☐

15 $\frac{1}{9}$ of 1,080 = ☐

16 $\frac{1}{9}$ of 810 = ☐

17 $\frac{1}{9}$ of 144 = ☐

18 $\frac{1}{9}$ of 270 = ☐

Adjust these ingredients lists by the amounts shown. Use the number facts if you need to.

Example

Pancake recipe	
1 person	**9 people**
100 g plain flour	900 g plain flour
2 large eggs	18 large eggs
300 ml milk	2,700 ml milk

x 9

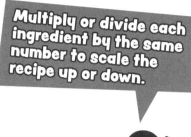

Multiply or divide each ingredient by the same number to scale the recipe up or down.

1   Milkshake recipe

2 people	**18 people**
200 ml milk	
3 bananas	
2 chocolate bars	

x 9

2   Flapjack recipe

1 flapjack traybake	**9 flapjack traybakes**
200 g oats	
120 g butter	
110 g brown sugar	

x 9

3   Fudge recipe

45 pieces	**5 pieces**
540 g sugar	
450 ml cream	
360 g butter	

÷ 9

4   Rock cakes recipe

27 rock cakes	**3 rock cakes**
270 g flour	
99 g sugar	
180 g butter	
90 g dried fruit	

÷ 9

5   Smoothie recipe

1 smoothie	**9 smoothies**
11 strawberries	
9 cherries	
50 ml yoghurt	
100 ml juice	

x 9

Calculations

Use this space for jottings and written calculations.

12

Find the perimeters of these regular polygons (not drawn to scale).

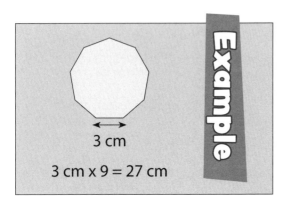

Example

3 cm

3 cm x 9 = 27 cm

Multiply the length of one side by the number of sides to find the perimeter of regular polygons.

1 6
2 7
3 8
4 9
5 0

1
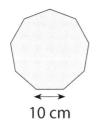
10 cm

Answer:

2
12 cm

Answer:

3
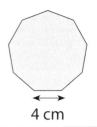
4 cm

Answer:

4
11 cm

Answer:

5

8 cm

Answer:

6
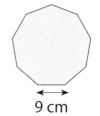
9 cm

Answer:

7
9 cm

Answer:

8
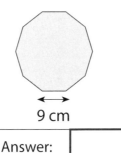
9 cm

Answer:

9
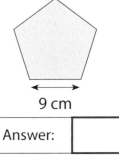
9 cm

Answer:

10
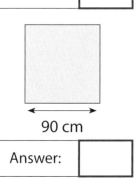
90 cm

Answer:

11
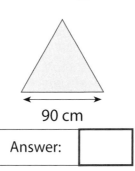
90 cm

Answer:

12
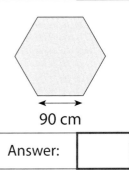
90 cm

Answer:

Can you see any patterns in the 10 times table?

1 Shade in or circle the multiples of 10 up to 100.

1	2	3	4	5	6	7	8	9	10
11	12	13	14	15	16	17	18	19	20
21	22	23	24	25	26	27	28	29	30
31	32	33	34	35	36	37	38	39	40
41	42	43	44	45	46	47	48	49	50
51	52	53	54	55	56	57	58	59	60
61	62	63	64	65	66	67	68	69	70
71	72	73	74	75	76	77	78	79	80
81	82	83	84	85	86	87	88	89	90
91	92	93	94	95	96	97	98	99	100

2 Find and circle the 10 times table in this number search.

1	x	10	=	10	3	80	100	2	4	12	2	6
11	11	1	x	10	=	100	9	x	50	x	x	40
7	x	x	6	2	110	5	x	10	5	10	10	10
70	x	10	10	x	4	x	10	=	40	=	=	7
5	100	10	=	=	10	10	=	30	8	10	20	9
120	x	3	=	110	100	=	80	10	x	x	11	x
8	110	10	x	80	1	50	60	120	10	10	120	10
x	60	100	=	10	x	10	=	100	=	=	110	=
10	11	x	10	60	=	110	90	20	90	40	8	90
=	12	x	10	=	120	30	3	x	10	=	40	9
80	120	6	x	12	=	40	7	x	10	=	70	30

Fill in the missing numbers.

Set 1

1	x	10	=	
	=	100	÷	10
	=	110	÷	10
	x	10	=	60
7	x	10	=	
12	x	10	=	
	=	1	x	10
	=	2	x	10
	=	30	÷	10
90	=		x	10

Set 2

100	=		x	10
4	x	10	=	
5	x	10	=	
	=	50	÷	10
6	=		÷	10
	=	11	x	10
120	=		x	10
	÷	10	=	1
	÷	10	=	2
8	x	10	=	

Set 3

	x	10	=	90
80	=		x	10
10	x	10	=	
	÷	10	=	12
4	=		÷	10
12	=		÷	10
60	÷	10	=	
	÷	10	=	10
	÷	10	=	11
40	=		x	10

Set 4

50	=		x	10
	=	6	x	10
11	x	10	=	
	÷	10	=	3
40	÷	10	=	
	÷	10	=	5
30	=		x	10
	=	7	x	10
	=	10	÷	10
2	=		÷	10

Set 5

1	=		÷	10
	=	20	÷	10
70	÷	10	=	
	÷	10	=	8
	÷	10	=	9
2	x	10	=	
	x	10	=	30
7	=		÷	10
	=	80	÷	10
9	=		÷	10

Set 6

	÷	10	=	12
4	=		÷	10
12	=		÷	10
60	÷	10	=	
100	÷	10	=	
	=	9	x	10
	=	10	x	10
4	x	10	=	
	x	10	=	50
5	=		÷	10

Set 7

30	÷	10	=	
	÷	10	=	4
6	=		÷	10
110	=		x	10
120	=		x	10
	÷	10	=	1
20	÷	10	=	
	÷	10	=	5
30	=		x	10
70	=		x	10

Set 8

	=	110	÷	10
5	=		÷	10
	=	60	÷	10
110	=		x	10
120	=		x	10
	÷	10	=	1
6	x	10	=	
	x	10	=	70
12	x	10	=	
10	=		x	10

Set 9

50	=		x	10
	=	6	x	10
	x	10	=	110
30	÷	10	=	
	÷	10	=	4
5	=		÷	10
	=	60	÷	10
110	=		x	10
50	÷	10	=	
30	=		x	10

1 **Complete the maze by drawing a line through multiples of 10. Watch out for dead ends!**

START HERE

10	40	60	90	45	43	68	96	24	20	87	46	40
34	42	46	30	100	35	75	36	97	35	88	53	25
43	20	120	70	34	78	97	110	24	66	86	120	75
24	35	65	110	67	33	24	120	77	90	57	35	35
65	30	78	120	10	80	60	30	65	40	80	54	98
23	54	10	46	30	64	77	90	43	57	86	99	64
78	23	34	110	36	46	54	10	60	90	50	65	36
90	85	65	35	74	76	45	20	46	64	34	35	87
90	50	33	85	24	100	30	40	43	30	5	88	40
87	36	100	57	86	22	53	60	47	7	67	97	54
54	96	35	7	60	34	65	30	40	80	70	20	**EXIT**

2 **Fill in the gaps in the table.**

a	10 + 10 + 10 + 10 + 10	5 x 10	50
b			120
c	10		10
d	10 + 10 + 10 + 10 + 10 + 10 + 10 + 10 + 10 + 10 + 10	11 x 10	
e			60
f	10 + 10		
g		10 x 10	
h	10 + 10 + 10 + 10 + 10 + 10 + 10		70
i			80
j	10 + 10 + 10 + 10		
k	10 + 10 + 10 + 10 + 10 + 10 + 10 + 10 + 10		
l			30

4

1 **Calculate the area of each of these rectangles (not drawn to scale).**

Example

10 cm

20 cm²

2 cm   10 cm x 2 cm = 20 cm²

a 10 cm / 7 cm

b 10 cm / 1 cm

c 9 cm / 10 cm

d 8 cm / 10 cm

e 10 cm / 10 cm

f 10 cm / 11 cm

g 5 cm / 10 cm

h 6 cm / 10 cm

i 10 cm / 3 cm

j 10 cm / 4 cm

k 12 cm / 10 cm

2 **Find the area of rectangles with these measurements.**

a	50 cm long and 10 cm wide	
b	10 cm long and 120 cm wide	
c	10 cm long and 40 cm wide	

1 Use the known multiplication facts to answer these questions.

Example

1 x 10 =	10
10 x 10 =	100
100 x 10 =	1,000

a

2 x 10 =	
20 x 10 =	
200 x 10 =	

b

3 x 10 =	
30 x 10 =	
300 x 10 =	

c

4 x 10 =	
40 x 10 =	
400 x 10 =	

d

5 x 10 =	
50 x 10 =	
500 x 10 =	

e

6 x 10 =	
60 x 10 =	
600 x 10 =	

f

7 x 10 =	
70 x 10 =	
700 x 10 =	

g

8 x 10 =	
80 x 10 =	
800 x 10 =	

h

9 x 10 =	
90 x 10 =	
900 x 10 =	

i

10 x 10 =	
100 x 10 =	
1,000 x 10 =	

j

11 x 10 =	
110 x 10 =	
1,100 x 10 =	

k

12 x 10 =	
120 x 10 =	
1,200 x 10 =	

2 Add in either x 10 or ÷ 10.

a	3		= 30
b	90		= 9
c	10		= 100
d	5		= 50
e	10		= 1
f	120		= 12

g	40		= 4
h	6		= 60
i	7		= 70
j	110		= 11
k	2		= 20
l	80		= 8

1

Match the times tables questions to the correct answers.

1 x 10		110
11 x 10		90
2 x 10		10
9 x 10		30
3 x 10		80
10 x 10		20
5 x 10		100
8 x 10		120
4 x 10		70
7 x 10		40
12 x 10		60
6 x 10		50

Now match the division questions to the correct answers.

30 ÷ 10		9
50 ÷ 10		1
10 ÷ 10		7
80 ÷ 10		3
90 ÷ 10		5
20 ÷ 10		12
70 ÷ 10		10
110 ÷ 10		2
100 ÷ 10		11
40 ÷ 10		8
120 ÷ 10		6
60 ÷ 10		4

2 **Solve these calculations and then put the answers in ascending order (smallest to greatest).**

a	4 x 10	3 x 10	100 x 10	120 ÷ 10	11 x 10
	40				
	smallest →	→	→	→	greatest
b	30 ÷ 10	11 x 10	2 x 10	1,200 ÷ 10	50 ÷ 10
	smallest →	→	→	→	greatest
c	60 x 10	50 ÷ 10	3 x 10	110 ÷ 10	90 x 10
	smallest →	→	→	→	greatest
d	80 ÷ 10	500 x 10	60 x 10	300 ÷ 10	12 x 10
	smallest →	→	→	→	greatest

Write the multiplication or division calculation and answer for each of these word problems.

1	There are 30 children in a class. They are split evenly into groups of 10. How many children will be in each group?	
2	5 children each have 10 pencils. How many pencils do they have altogether?	
3	There are 10 children in a group. They evenly share 10 sweets between themselves. How many sweets will they have each?	
4	Games come in boxes of 10. How many games will there be in 12 boxes?	
5	There are 80 biscuits in a bag. A woman shares them equally between her 10 dogs. How many will they get each?	
6	Bookshelves hold 10 books each. How many shelves will be needed to hold 110 books?	
7	There are 10 years in a decade. How many years are there in 8 decades?	
8	If a bag can hold 10 marbles, how many bags will be needed to hold 90 marbles?	
9	There are 10 spots on each cushion. How many spots will there be on 4 cushions?	
10	A group of 10 children each eat 15 sweets. How many sweets are eaten in total?	
11	There are 30 children in each class in a school. If there are 10 classes, how many children are there altogether in the school?	
12	A picture book has 10 pages. How many pages will 120 copies of the book have?	
13	A decagon has 10 sides. How many sides will 80 decagons have?	
14	A group of 450 people are separated into 10 equal groups. How many people will be in each group?	

8

Use the 10 times table to find these equivalent fractions.

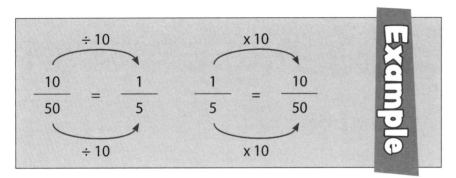

Multiply or divide the numerator and the denominator by the same number.

1 $\dfrac{2}{3} = \dfrac{20}{\Box}$

2 $\dfrac{70}{80} = \dfrac{\Box}{8}$

3 $\dfrac{3}{5} = \dfrac{\Box}{50}$

4 $\dfrac{\Box}{120} = \dfrac{11}{12}$

5 $\dfrac{10}{\Box} = \dfrac{100}{110}$

6 $\dfrac{\Box}{50} = \dfrac{4}{5}$

7 $\dfrac{20}{80} = \dfrac{2}{\Box}$

8 $\dfrac{\Box}{12} = \dfrac{40}{120}$

9 $\dfrac{3}{11} = \dfrac{30}{\Box}$

10 $\dfrac{10}{60} = \dfrac{\Box}{6}$

11 $\dfrac{10}{40} = \dfrac{1}{\Box}$

12 $\dfrac{1}{\Box} = \dfrac{10}{70}$

13 $\dfrac{5}{11} = \dfrac{\Box}{110}$

14 $\dfrac{50}{\Box} = \dfrac{5}{8}$

15 $\dfrac{10}{50} = \dfrac{1}{\Box}$

16 $\dfrac{\Box}{11} = \dfrac{30}{110}$

17 $\dfrac{9}{12} = \dfrac{90}{\Box}$

18 $\dfrac{\Box}{7} = \dfrac{40}{70}$

19 $\dfrac{8}{11} = \dfrac{80}{\Box}$

20 $\dfrac{50}{60} = \dfrac{\Box}{6}$

21 $\dfrac{100}{110} = \dfrac{10}{\Box}$

22 $\dfrac{\Box}{9} = \dfrac{50}{90}$

Use the given fraction to find the whole number.

Example

$\frac{1}{10}$ of | 80 | is 8

| 8 | 8 | 8 | 8 | 8 | 8 | 8 | 8 | 8 | 8 |
| 80 |

1 $\frac{1}{10}$ of ☐ is 7

| 7 | | | | | | | | | |

2 $\frac{1}{10}$ of ☐ is 4

| 4 | | | | | | | | | |

3 $\frac{1}{10}$ of ☐ is 3

| 3 | | | | | | | | | |

4 $\frac{1}{10}$ of ☐ is 11

| 11 | | | | | | | | | |

5 $\frac{1}{10}$ of ☐ is 10

| 10 | | | | | | | | | |

6 $\frac{1}{10}$ of ☐ is 12

| 12 | | | | | | | | | |

7 $\frac{1}{10}$ of ☐ is 9

| 9 | | | | | | | | | |

8 $\frac{1}{10}$ of ☐ is 6

| 6 | | | | | | | | | |

9 $\frac{1}{10}$ of ☐ is 2

10 $\frac{1}{10}$ of ☐ is 5

11 $\frac{1}{10}$ of ☐ is 25

12 $\frac{1}{10}$ of ☐ is 20

13 $\frac{1}{10}$ of ☐ is 50

14 $\frac{1}{10}$ of ☐ is 13

15 $\frac{1}{10}$ of ☐ is 15

16 $\frac{1}{10}$ of ☐ is 60

17 $\frac{1}{10}$ of ☐ is 30

18 $\frac{1}{10}$ of ☐ is 40

10 TIMES TABLE 10

Find $\frac{1}{10}$ of the numbers below by dividing them by 10.

Example

$\frac{1}{10}$ of 50 = $\boxed{5}$

5	5	5	5	5	5	5	5	5	5
				50					

1 $\frac{1}{10}$ of 70 = $\boxed{}$

2 $\frac{1}{10}$ of 20 = $\boxed{}$

3 $\frac{1}{10}$ of 100 = $\boxed{}$

4 $\frac{1}{10}$ of 30 = $\boxed{}$

5 $\frac{1}{10}$ of 80 = $\boxed{}$

6 $\frac{1}{10}$ of 60 = $\boxed{}$

7 $\frac{1}{10}$ of 110 = $\boxed{}$

8 $\frac{1}{10}$ of 90 = $\boxed{}$

9 $\frac{1}{10}$ of 10 = $\boxed{}$

10 $\frac{1}{10}$ of 120 = $\boxed{}$

11 $\frac{1}{10}$ of 40 = $\boxed{}$

12 $\frac{1}{10}$ of 800 = $\boxed{}$

13 $\frac{1}{10}$ of 1,000 = $\boxed{}$

14 $\frac{1}{10}$ of 1,200 = $\boxed{}$

15 $\frac{1}{10}$ of 300 = $\boxed{}$

16 $\frac{1}{10}$ of 1,100 = $\boxed{}$

17 $\frac{1}{10}$ of 770 = $\boxed{}$

18 $\frac{1}{10}$ of 700 = $\boxed{}$

Adjust these ingredients lists by the amounts shown. Use the number facts if you need to.

Example

Pancake recipe	
1 person	**10 people**
100 g plain flour	1,000 g plain flour
2 large eggs	20 large eggs
300 ml milk	3,000 ml milk

x 10

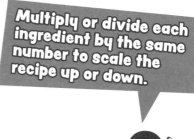

Multiply or divide each ingredient by the same number to scale the recipe up or down.

1

Milkshake recipe	
2 people	**20 people**
200 ml milk	
3 bananas	
2 chocolate bars	

x 10

2

Flapjack recipe	
1 flapjack traybake	**10 flapjack traybakes**
200 g oats	
120 g butter	
110 g brown sugar	

x 10

3

Fudge recipe	
50 pieces	**5 pieces**
400 g sugar	
500 ml cream	
300 g butter	

÷ 10

4

Rock cakes recipe	
30 rock cakes	**3 rock cakes**
200 g flour	
70 g sugar	
200 g butter	
80 g dried fruit	

÷ 10

5

Smoothie recipe	
1 smoothie	**10 smoothies**
11 strawberries	
9 cherries	
50 ml yoghurt	
100 ml juice	

x 10

Calculations

Use this space for jottings and written calculations.

 12

Find the perimeters of these regular polygons (not drawn to scale).

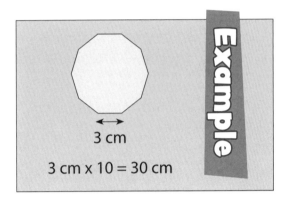

Example

3 cm

3 cm x 10 = 30 cm

Multiply the length of one side by the number of sides to find the perimeter of regular polygons.

1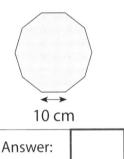

10 cm

Answer:

2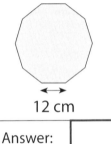

12 cm

Answer:

3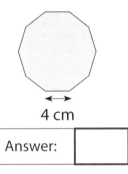

4 cm

Answer:

4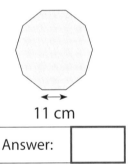

11 cm

Answer:

5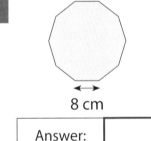

8 cm

Answer:

6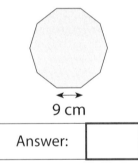

9 cm

Answer:

7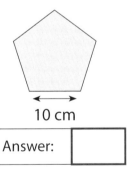

10 cm

Answer:

8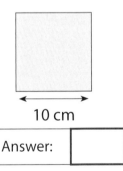

10 cm

Answer:

9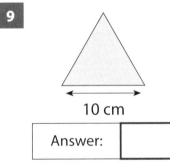

10 cm

Answer:

10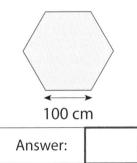

100 cm

Answer:

11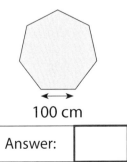

100 cm

Answer:

12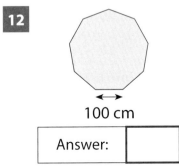

100 cm

Answer:

11 TIMES TABLE

Can you see any patterns in the 11 times table?

1 Shade in or circle the multiples of 11 up to 100.

1	2	3	4	5	6	7	8	9	10
11	12	13	14	15	16	17	18	19	20
21	22	23	24	25	26	27	28	29	30
31	32	33	34	35	36	37	38	39	40
41	42	43	44	45	46	47	48	49	50
51	52	53	54	55	56	57	58	59	60
61	62	63	64	65	66	67	68	69	70
71	72	73	74	75	76	77	78	79	80
81	82	83	84	85	86	87	88	89	90
91	92	93	94	95	96	97	98	99	100

2 Find and circle the 11 times table in this number search.

1	x	11	=	11	4	22	110	3	8	1	x	11
9	88	10	x	11	=	5	132	121	7	x	77	88
99	11	8	12	10	x	11	x	55	x	11	11	121
110	11	x	77	x	132	4	77	11	11	=	66	=
4	x	11	2	33	11	110	33	10	=	22	77	3
4	11	=	4	x	11	=	44	x	77	55	121	x
x	=	77	8	110	11	66	132	11	3	8	9	11
11	121	88	55	x	x	=	121	=	x	x	x	=
=	132	5	x	11	11	x	22	110	11	11	11	33
66	2	x	11	=	33	=	11	44	=	=	=	11
3	6	x	11	=	66	22	88	132	44	99	99	88

11 TIMES TABLE

2

Fill in the missing numbers.

Set 1

132	÷	11	=	
1	=		÷	11
	=	22	÷	11
3	=		÷	11
4	=		÷	11
	x	11	=	66
7	x	11	=	
5	x	11	=	
	÷	11	=	4
55	÷	11	=	

Set 2

	÷	11	=	6
8	x	11	=	
	÷	11	=	3
5	=		÷	11
6	=		÷	11
3	x	11	=	
	x	11	=	44
	=	4	x	11
1	x	11	=	
	x	11	=	110

Set 3

11	x	11	=	
	=	7	x	11
88	=		x	11
	÷	11	=	7
88	÷	11	=	
	÷	11	=	9
110	÷	11	=	
	÷	11	=	11
	=	5	x	11
66	=		x	11

Set 4

	=	77	÷	11
8	=		÷	11
	=	99	÷	11
10	=		÷	11
11	=		÷	11
	=	132	÷	11
12	x	11	=	
33	=		x	11
	=	9	x	11
110	=		x	11

Set 5

	=	9	x	11
110	=		x	11
	=	11	x	11
132	=		x	11
11	÷	11	=	
	÷	11	=	1
2	x	11	=	
	x	11	=	99
11	=		x	11
22	=		x	11

Set 6

	÷	11	=	8
99	÷	11	=	
110	÷	11	=	
	÷	11	=	11
55	=		x	11
	=	66	÷	11
3	x	11	=	
	x	11	=	44
44	=		x	11
1	x	11	=	

Set 7

66	=		x	11
	=	77	÷	11
8	=		÷	11
	=	99	÷	11
10	=		÷	11
11	=		÷	11
	=	132	÷	11
12	x	11	=	
	=	3	x	11
99	=		x	11

Set 8

	x	11	=	77
5	x	11	=	
77	=		x	11
	=	8	x	11
77	÷	11	=	
88	÷	11	=	
	÷	11	=	9
	÷	11	=	4
55	÷	11	=	
	÷	11	=	6

Set 9

2	=		÷	11
	=	33	÷	11
4	=		÷	11
	x	11	=	66
	÷	11	=	5
66	÷	11	=	
8	x	11	=	
33	÷	11	=	
5	=		÷	11
	x	11	=	77

1 **Complete the maze by drawing a line through multiples of 11. Watch out for dead ends!**

START HERE

66	34	34	132	33	56	32	77	22	75	24	64	121
22	32	66	34	45	32	77	32	75	121	99	65	132
55	25	89	64	77	66	78	43	35	77	15	110	46
33	88	76	46	88	6	46	45	56	54	76	132	86
77	99	22	110	121	132	11	22	45	75	43	121	34
56	11	46	88	75	92	34	55	77	99	88	66	24
23	22	86	35	76	37	85	34	33	32	24	44	74
32	77	57	74	22	66	44	24	55	45	44	55	77
77	35	43	7	34	33	86	46	36	75	35	33	43
56	32	65	66	75	35	77	22	66	25	86	121	46
63	45	23	88	110	43	67	43	78	32	54	132	**EXIT**

2 **Fill in the gaps in the table.**

a	11 + 11 + 11 + 11 + 11 + 11 + 11	7 x 11	77
b			33
c	11 + 11 + 11 + 11 + 11 + 11 + 11 + 11		
d	11 + 11 + 11 + 11 + 11		55
e		10 x 11	
f	11 + 11		
g			132
h		9 x 11	
i	11 + 11 + 11 + 11 + 11 + 11 + 11 + 11 + 11 + 11 + 11		121
j	11		11
k	11 + 11 + 11 + 11 + 11 + 11		
l			44

4

1 Calculate the area of each of these rectangles (not drawn to scale).

Example

11 cm

22 cm² | 2 cm | 11 cm x 2 cm = 22 cm²

a 11 cm / 9 cm

b 11 cm / 1 cm

c 11 cm / 11 cm

d 11 cm / 10 cm

e 12 cm / 11 cm

f 11 cm / 5 cm

g 3 cm / 11 cm

h 4 cm / 11 cm

i 11 cm / 6 cm

j 8 cm / 11 cm

k 7 cm / 11 cm

2 Find the area of rectangles with these measurements.

Ninja Challenge

a	50 cm long and 11 cm wide	
b	11 cm long and 120 cm wide	
c	11 cm long and 40 cm wide	

1 **Use the known multiplication facts to answer these questions.**

Example	
1 x 11 =	11
10 x 11 =	110
100 x 11 =	1,100

a

2 x 11 =	
20 x 11 =	
200 x 11 =	

b

3 x 11 =	
30 x 11 =	
300 x 11 =	

c

4 x 11 =	
40 x 11 =	
400 x 11 =	

d

5 x 11 =	
50 x 11 =	
500 x 11 =	

e

6 x 11 =	
60 x 11 =	
600 x 11 =	

f

7 x 11 =	
70 x 11 =	
700 x 11 =	

g

8 x 11 =	
80 x 11 =	
800 x 11 =	

h

9 x 11 =	
90 x 11 =	
900 x 11 =	

i

10 x 11 =	
100 x 11 =	
1,000 x 11 =	

j

11 x 11 =	
110 x 11 =	
1,100 x 11 =	

k

12 x 11 =	
120 x 11 =	
1,200 x 11 =	

2 **Use the known multiplication facts to answer these questions.**

Example 36 x 11	
30 x 11	330
6 x 11	66
Total:	396

a 28 x 11

20 x 11	
8 x 11	
Total:	

b 75 x 11

70 x 11	
5 x 11	
Total:	

c 39 x 11

30 x 11	
9 x 11	
Total:	

d 57 x 11

50 x 11	
7 x 11	
Total:	

e 48 x 11

40 x 11	
8 x 11	
Total:	

f 284 x 11

200 x 11	
80 x 11	
4 x 11	
Total:	

g 472 x 11

400 x 11	
70 x 11	
2 x 11	
Total:	

h 395 x 11

300 x 11	
90 x 11	
5 x 11	
Total:	

6

Complete these short division questions using the 11 times table.

Example

$858 \div 11 = 78$

```
        0   7   8
11 | 8  ⁸5  ⁸8
```

You could write out the times table to help you with these questions.

1
```
11 | 7   5   9
```

2
```
11 | 9   3   5
```

3
```
11 | 8   6   9
```

4
```
11 | 1   3   3   1
```

5
```
11 | 1   6   7   2
```

6
```
11 | 2   7   8   3
```

7
```
11 | 2   4   7   5
```

8
```
11 | 2   3   5   4
```

9
```
11 | 3   9   8   2
```

10	1,562	÷	11	=
11	3,916	÷	11	=
12	2,365	÷	11	=
13	7,194	÷	11	=

14	2,772	÷	11	=
15	2,695	÷	11	=
16	4,015	÷	11	=
17	3,146	÷	11	=

Calculations

Use this space for jottings and written calculations.

Write the multiplication or division calculation and answer for each of these word problems.

1	There are 132 counters in a box. 11 children share the counters equally between themselves. How many counters will they receive each?	
2	11 children each make 5 boxes. How many boxes do they make altogether?	
3	A bag holds 11 bananas. How many bags will be needed to hold 77 bananas?	
4	It takes 11 minutes for a machine to make a toy. How many toys can the machine make in 121 minutes?	
5	A leaflet has 11 pages. How many pages will there be in 8 leaflets?	
6	There are 11 pots on a table. If 11 pencils are shared equally between the pots, how many will be in each?	
7	If there are 11 raisins in each box, how many raisins will there be in 6 boxes?	
8	A rare breed of plant flowers every 11 years. How many times will it flower in 110 years?	
9	Each child in a group needs 11 sheets of paper. How many sheets will be needed for 11 children?	
10	A group of people are split into teams of 11. If there are 40 teams, how many people are there in total?	
11	A baker has 660 g of flour. If each biscuit requires 11 g of flour, how many biscuits can be made?	
12	There are 11 classes in a school. If there are 30 children in each class, how many children are there in total?	
13	A group of 11 children each raise £80 for charity. How much do they raise altogether?	
14	A box of 1,210 pencils is split evenly between 11 pots. How many pencils will there be in each pot?	

8

Use the 11 times table to find these equivalent fractions.

$$\xrightarrow{\div 11}$$

$$\frac{11}{55} = \frac{1}{5} \qquad \frac{1}{5} = \frac{11}{55}$$

$$\xrightarrow{\div 11} \qquad \xrightarrow{x\,11}$$

Multiply or divide the numerator and the denominator by the same number.

1 $\dfrac{2}{3} = \dfrac{22}{\square}$

2 $\dfrac{77}{88} = \dfrac{7}{\square}$

3 $\dfrac{3}{5} = \dfrac{\square}{55}$

4 $\dfrac{121}{132} = \dfrac{11}{\square}$

5 $\dfrac{\square}{121} = \dfrac{10}{11}$

6 $\dfrac{44}{55} = \dfrac{4}{\square}$

7 $\dfrac{22}{88} = \dfrac{\square}{8}$

8 $\dfrac{4}{\square} = \dfrac{44}{132}$

9 $\dfrac{3}{11} = \dfrac{\square}{121}$

10 $\dfrac{11}{\square} = \dfrac{1}{6}$

11 $\dfrac{11}{44} = \dfrac{\square}{4}$

12 $\dfrac{1}{7} = \dfrac{11}{\square}$

13 $\dfrac{5}{11} = \dfrac{\square}{121}$

14 $\dfrac{\square}{88} = \dfrac{5}{8}$

15 $\dfrac{11}{55} = \dfrac{1}{\square}$

16 $\dfrac{\square}{11} = \dfrac{33}{121}$

17 $\dfrac{9}{12} = \dfrac{99}{\square}$

18 $\dfrac{\square}{7} = \dfrac{44}{77}$

19 $\dfrac{8}{11} = \dfrac{\square}{121}$

20 $\dfrac{55}{66} = \dfrac{\square}{6}$

21 $\dfrac{110}{121} = \dfrac{10}{\square}$

22 $\dfrac{\square}{9} = \dfrac{55}{99}$

9 11 TIMES TABLE

Use the given fraction to find the whole number.

Example $\frac{1}{11}$ of $\boxed{88}$ is 8

8	8	8	8	8	8	8	8	8	8	8

88

1 $\frac{1}{11}$ of $\boxed{}$ is 7

7										

2 $\frac{1}{11}$ of $\boxed{}$ is 4

4										

3 $\frac{1}{11}$ of $\boxed{}$ is 3

3										

4 $\frac{1}{11}$ of $\boxed{}$ is 11

11										

5 $\frac{1}{11}$ of $\boxed{}$ is 10

10										

6 $\frac{1}{11}$ of $\boxed{}$ is 12

12										

7 $\frac{1}{11}$ of $\boxed{}$ is 9

9										

8 $\frac{1}{11}$ of $\boxed{}$ is 6

6										

9 $\frac{1}{11}$ of $\boxed{}$ is 2

10 $\frac{1}{11}$ of $\boxed{}$ is 5

11 $\frac{1}{11}$ of $\boxed{}$ is 25

12 $\frac{1}{11}$ of $\boxed{}$ is 20

13 $\frac{1}{11}$ of $\boxed{}$ is 50

14 $\frac{1}{11}$ of $\boxed{}$ is 70

15 $\frac{1}{11}$ of $\boxed{}$ is 30

16 $\frac{1}{11}$ of $\boxed{}$ is 110

17 $\frac{1}{11}$ of $\boxed{}$ is 60

18 $\frac{1}{11}$ of $\boxed{}$ is 1,000

11 TIMES TABLE

 10

Find $\frac{1}{11}$ of the numbers below by dividing them by 11.

Example
$\frac{1}{11}$ of 66 = $\boxed{6}$

6	6	6	6	6	6	6	6	6	6	6

66

1 $\frac{1}{11}$ of 33 = $\boxed{}$

2 $\frac{1}{11}$ of 99 = $\boxed{}$

3 $\frac{1}{11}$ of 44 = $\boxed{}$

4 $\frac{1}{11}$ of 77 = $\boxed{}$

5 $\frac{1}{11}$ of 121 = $\boxed{}$

6 $\frac{1}{11}$ of 55 = $\boxed{}$

7 $\frac{1}{11}$ of 110 = $\boxed{}$

8 $\frac{1}{11}$ of 132 = $\boxed{}$

9 $\frac{1}{11}$ of 88 = $\boxed{}$

10 $\frac{1}{11}$ of 11 = $\boxed{}$

11 $\frac{1}{11}$ of 22 = $\boxed{}$

12 $\frac{1}{11}$ of 143 = $\boxed{}$

13 $\frac{1}{11}$ of 165 = $\boxed{}$

14 $\frac{1}{11}$ of 220 = $\boxed{}$

15 $\frac{1}{11}$ of 275 = $\boxed{}$

16 $\frac{1}{11}$ of 330 = $\boxed{}$

17 $\frac{1}{11}$ of 1,100 = $\boxed{}$

18 $\frac{1}{11}$ of 550 = $\boxed{}$

Adjust these ingredients lists by the amounts shown. Use the number facts if you need to.

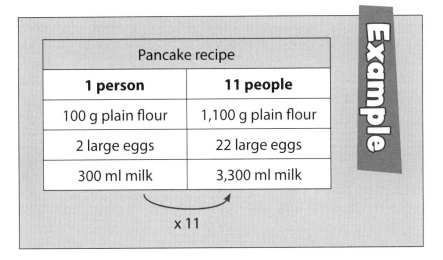

Example

Pancake recipe	
1 person	**11 people**
100 g plain flour	1,100 g plain flour
2 large eggs	22 large eggs
300 ml milk	3,300 ml milk

x 11

Multiply or divide each ingredient by the same number to scale the recipe up or down.

1

Milkshake recipe	
2 people	**22 people**
300 ml milk	
3 bananas	
2 chocolate bars	

x 11

2

Flapjack recipe	
1 flapjack traybake	**11 flapjack traybakes**
200 g oats	
120 g butter	
110 g brown sugar	

x 11

3

Fudge recipe	
55 pieces	**5 pieces**
440 g sugar	
550 ml cream	
330 g butter	

÷ 11

4

Rock cakes recipe	
33 rock cakes	**3 rock cakes**
220 g flour	
77 g sugar	
220 g butter	
110 g dried fruit	

÷ 11

5

Smoothie recipe	
1 smoothie	**11 smoothies**
11 strawberries	
9 cherries	
50 ml yoghurt	
100 ml juice	

x 11

Calculations

Use this space for jottings and written calculations.

Find the perimeters of these regular polygons (not drawn to scale).

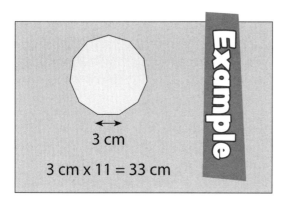

Example

3 cm

3 cm x 11 = 33 cm

Multiply the length of one side by the number of sides to find the perimeter of regular polygons.

1
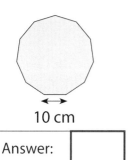
10 cm
Answer:

2
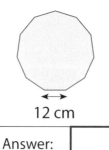
12 cm
Answer:

3
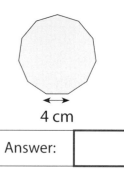
4 cm
Answer:

4
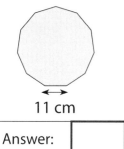
11 cm
Answer:

5
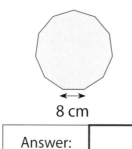
8 cm
Answer:

6
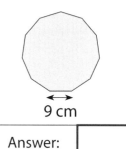
9 cm
Answer:

7
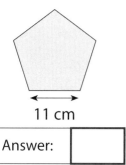
11 cm
Answer:

8
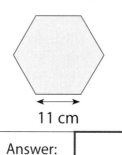
11 cm
Answer:

9
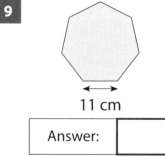
11 cm
Answer:

10
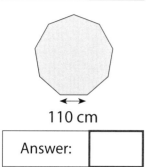
110 cm
Answer:

11
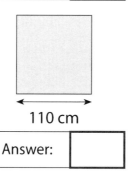
110 cm
Answer:

12
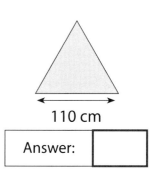
110 cm
Answer:

12 TIMES TABLE

Can you see any patterns in the 12 times table?

1 **Shade in or circle the multiples of 12 up to 100.**

1	2	3	4	5	6	7	8	9	10
11	12	13	14	15	16	17	18	19	20
21	22	23	24	25	26	27	28	29	30
31	32	33	34	35	36	37	38	39	40
41	42	43	44	45	46	47	48	49	50
51	52	53	54	55	56	57	58	59	60
61	62	63	64	65	66	67	68	69	70
71	72	73	74	75	76	77	78	79	80
81	82	83	84	85	86	87	88	89	90
91	92	93	94	95	96	97	98	99	100

2 **Find and circle the 12 times table in this number search.**

1	x	12	=	12	6	10	4	x	12	=	60	5
12	10	x	12	=	x	x	4	96	48	6	84	x
4	108	12	3	2	12	12	144	x	120	x	132	12
3	120	=	9	x	=	=	2	1	12	12	84	=
5	x	144	x	12	12	120	8	x	72	=	36	72
11	36	12	12	=	144	=	12	x	12	72	48	8
x	144	60	=	24	8	7	36	132	12	=	144	x
12	96	132	120	24	9	x	12	=	108	=	48	12
=	7	x	12	=	84	11	x	12	=	84	70	=
132	12	x	12	=	7	x	12	=	72	132	120	96
1	x	12	=	36	84	5	x	12	=	60	24	120

Fill in the missing numbers.

Set 1

7	x	12	=	
	x	12	=	96
9	x	12	=	
11	=		÷	12
	=	144	÷	12
	x	12	=	12
2	x	12	=	
3	x	12	=	
	x	12	=	48
24	=		x	12

Set 2

	÷	12	=	10
36	=		x	12
	=	4	x	12
	x	12	=	120
48	÷	12	=	
60	÷	12	=	
	÷	12	=	6
84	÷	12	=	
	÷	12	=	11
	÷	12	=	12

Set 3

1	=		÷	12
11	x	12	=	
	÷	12	=	9
2	=		÷	12
3	=		÷	12
	=	1	x	12
60	=		x	12
	=	6	x	12
4	=		÷	12
12	x	12	=	

Set 4

5	x	12	=	
	x	12	=	72
	=	9	x	12
	=	10	x	12
132	=		x	12
	=	12	x	12
	÷	12	=	1
84	=		x	12
96	=		x	12
	÷	12	=	2

Set 5

8	=		÷	12
	=	108	÷	12
10	=		÷	12
108	=		x	12
	=	10	x	12
132	=		x	12
60	÷	12	=	
	÷	12	=	6
84	÷	12	=	
	÷	12	=	11

Set 6

144	=		x	12
	÷	12	=	1
	=	7	x	12
96	=		x	12
24	÷	12	=	
	÷	12	=	3
96	÷	12	=	
5	=		÷	12
6	=		÷	12
	=	84	÷	12

Set 7

12	=		x	12
	=	5	x	12
72	=		x	12
	=	2	x	12
	=	3	x	12
48	=		x	12
10	x	12	=	
120	÷	12	=	
4	=		÷	12
12	x	12	=	

Set 8

	=	11	x	12
12	=		÷	12
1	x	12	=	
	x	12	=	24
120	=		x	12
	=	12	x	12
12	÷	12	=	
84	=		x	12
	x	12	=	36
4	x	12	=	

Set 9

	÷	12	=	10
3	x	12	=	
	x	12	=	48
	=	2	x	12
	=	3	x	12
48	=		x	12
	÷	12	=	4
60	÷	12	=	
72	÷	12	=	
	÷	12	=	7

1 Complete the maze by drawing a line through multiples of 12. Watch out for dead ends!

START HERE

12	34	44	26	86	96	22	75	60	72	84	96	56
72	6	24	43	56	77	12	24	36	86	43	108	43
96	43	56	65	34	65	72	54	24	54	87	120	67
108	144	96	36	48	120	132	24	31	65	24	132	33
67	86	84	46	96	14	12	57	72	22	54	144	24
44	35	108	66	84	132	43	53	24	35	46	60	65
31	87	120	45	46	14	75	45	48	54	65	72	32
146	44	4	6	43	144	23	36	72	84	120	96	54
44	67	75	4	120	75	43	60	22	32	27	48	19
24	24	6	34	144	35	36	132	44	42	63	58	73
76	124	54	44	32	12	64	144	12	36	24	96	**EXIT**

2 Fill in the gaps in the table.

a	12 + 12 + 12 + 12 + 12	5 x 12	60
b			96
c	12 + 12 + 12 + 12 + 12 + 12		72
d	12		
e		12 x 12	
f	12 + 12 + 12 + 12 + 12 + 12 + 12 + 12 + 12		108
g			132
h	12 + 12 + 12		
i	12 + 12 + 12 + 12 + 12 + 12 + 12		84
j			24
k	12 + 12 + 12 + 12 + 12 + 12 + 12 + 12 + 12 + 12		
l		4 x 12	

1 Calculate the area of each of these rectangles (not drawn to scale).

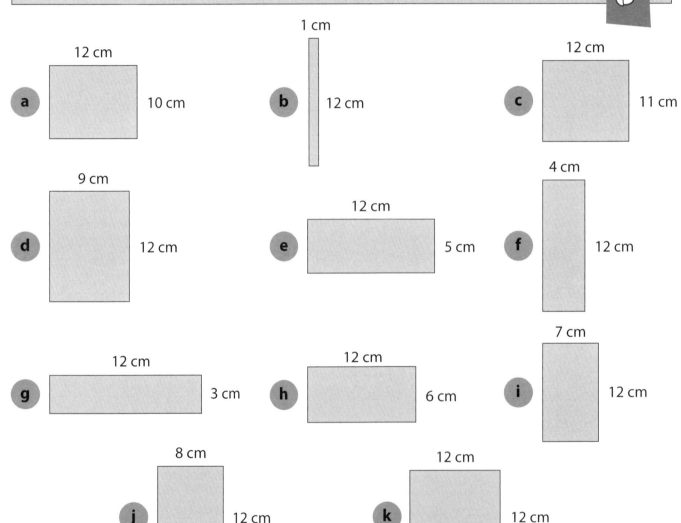

Example

12 cm

24 cm² 2 cm 12 cm x 2 cm = 24 cm²

a 12 cm / 10 cm

b 1 cm / 12 cm

c 12 cm / 11 cm

d 9 cm / 12 cm

e 12 cm / 5 cm

f 4 cm / 12 cm

g 12 cm / 3 cm

h 12 cm / 6 cm

i 7 cm / 12 cm

j 8 cm / 12 cm

k 12 cm / 12 cm

2 Find the area of rectangles with these measurements.

a	50 cm long and 12 cm wide	
b	12 cm long and 120 cm wide	
c	120 cm long and 40 cm wide	

Ninja Challenge

1 Use the known multiplication facts to answer these questions.

Example

1 x 12 =	12
10 x 12 =	120
100 x 12 =	1,200

a

2 x 12 =	
20 x 12 =	
200 x 12 =	

b

3 x 12 =	
30 x 12 =	
300 x 12 =	

c

4 x 12 =	
40 x 12 =	
400 x 12 =	

d

5 x 12 =	
50 x 12 =	
500 x 12 =	

e

6 x 12 =	
60 x 12 =	
600 x 12 =	

f

7 x 12 =	
70 x 12 =	
700 x 12 =	

g

8 x 12 =	
80 x 12 =	
800 x 12 =	

h

9 x 12 =	
90 x 12 =	
900 x 12 =	

i

10 x 12 =	
100 x 12 =	
1,000 x 12 =	

j

11 x 12 =	
110 x 12 =	
1,100 x 12 =	

k

12 x 12 =	
120 x 12 =	
1,200 x 12 =	

2 Use the known multiplication facts to answer these questions.

Example

36 x 12	
30 x 12	360
6 x 12	72
Total:	432

a

28 x 12	
20 x 12	
8 x 12	
Total:	

b

75 x 12	
70 x 12	
5 x 12	
Total:	

c

39 x 12	
30 x 12	
9 x 12	
Total:	

d

57 x 12	
50 x 12	
7 x 12	
Total:	

e

48 x 12	
40 x 12	
8 x 12	
Total:	

f

284 x 12	
200 x 12	
80 x 12	
4 x 12	
Total:	

g

472 x 12	
400 x 12	
70 x 12	
2 x 12	
Total:	

h

395 x 12	
300 x 12	
90 x 12	
5 x 12	
Total:	

12 TIMES TABLE

 6

Complete these short division questions using the 12 times table.

Example

$912 \div 12 = 76$

```
        0    7    6
12 |  9   ⁹1   ⁷2
```

You could write out the times table to help you with these questions.

1
```
12 |  8   2   8
```

2
```
12 |  7   0   8
```

3
```
12 |  1   7   4   0
```

4
```
12 |  1   5   2   4
```

5
```
12 |  1   3   6   8
```

6
```
12 |  1   9   8   0
```

7
```
12 |  1   4   1   6
```

8
```
12 |  2   7   3   6
```

9
```
12 |  2   2   3   2
```

10	1,836	÷	12	=
11	3,216	÷	12	=
12	2,100	÷	12	=
13	6,936	÷	12	=

14	5,700	÷	12	=
15	3,096	÷	12	=
16	2,028	÷	12	=
17	2,964	÷	12	=

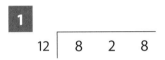 **Calculations**

Use this space for jottings and written calculations.

7

12 TIMES TABLE

Write the multiplication or division calculation and answer for each of these word problems.

1	There are 12 months in a year. How many months are there in 8 years?	
2	Bread rolls come in packs of 12. If 108 rolls are needed, how many packs will have to be bought?	
3	Strawberries come in punnets of 12. How many strawberries will there be in 7 punnets?	
4	There are 36 children in a class. If they are put into 12 equal groups, how many children will be in each group?	
5	There are 12 children in a group. Each one needs 6 sheets of paper. How many sheets of paper will be needed?	
6	1 kg of potatoes costs £2. How much will 12 kg cost?	
7	A butterfly has 12 spots on each wing. How many spots will there be on 2 butterflies?	
8	A family has a set of triplets. Each triplet has 12 cuddly toys. How many cuddly toys are there in total?	
9	A TV show has 12 episodes in each season. How many episodes will there be in 5 seasons?	
10	A child is 180 months old. How old is this in years?	
11	A box of marbles is split equally into 12 bags. If there are 360 marbles in total, how many will there be in each bag?	
12	12 children each need 20 counters. How many counters are needed in total?	
13	A group of people share £960 equally between themselves. If each child receives £12, how many people are in the group?	
14	Each child in a class of 30 makes 12 biscuits. How many biscuits are there in total?	

8

Use the 12 times table to find these equivalent fractions.

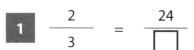

Example

Multiply or divide the numerator and the denominator by the same number.

$$\underset{\div 12}{\overset{\div 12}{\frac{12}{60}}} = \frac{1}{5} \qquad \underset{\times 12}{\overset{\times 12}{\frac{1}{5}}} = \frac{12}{60}$$

1 $\dfrac{2}{3} = \dfrac{24}{\boxed{}}$

2 $\dfrac{84}{96} = \dfrac{\boxed{}}{8}$

3 $\dfrac{3}{5} = \dfrac{36}{\boxed{}}$

4 $\dfrac{132}{144} = \dfrac{\boxed{}}{12}$

5 $\dfrac{120}{132} = \dfrac{\boxed{}}{11}$

6 $\dfrac{48}{\boxed{}} = \dfrac{4}{5}$

7 $\dfrac{24}{96} = \dfrac{\boxed{}}{8}$

8 $\dfrac{4}{12} = \dfrac{48}{\boxed{}}$

9 $\dfrac{3}{11} = \dfrac{\boxed{}}{132}$

10 $\dfrac{12}{\boxed{}} = \dfrac{1}{6}$

11 $\dfrac{12}{48} = \dfrac{\boxed{}}{4}$

12 $\dfrac{1}{7} = \dfrac{12}{\boxed{}}$

13 $\dfrac{\boxed{}}{11} = \dfrac{60}{132}$

14 $\dfrac{60}{96} = \dfrac{5}{\boxed{}}$

15 $\dfrac{12}{60} = \dfrac{1}{\boxed{}}$

16 $\dfrac{\boxed{}}{11} = \dfrac{36}{132}$

17 $\dfrac{9}{\boxed{}} = \dfrac{108}{144}$

18 $\dfrac{4}{7} = \dfrac{48}{\boxed{}}$

19 $\dfrac{8}{11} = \dfrac{\boxed{}}{132}$

20 $\dfrac{60}{72} = \dfrac{5}{\boxed{}}$

21 $\dfrac{120}{132} = \dfrac{\boxed{}}{11}$

22 $\dfrac{5}{9} = \dfrac{60}{\boxed{}}$

Use the given fraction to find the whole number.

Example $\frac{1}{12}$ of ☐ 96 is 8

| 8 | 8 | 8 | 8 | 8 | 8 | 8 | 8 | 8 | 8 | 8 | 8 |
| 96 |

1 $\frac{1}{12}$ of ☐ is 7

| 7 |

2 $\frac{1}{12}$ of ☐ is 4

| 4 |

3 $\frac{1}{12}$ of ☐ is 3

| 3 |

4 $\frac{1}{12}$ of ☐ is 11

| 11 |

5 $\frac{1}{12}$ of ☐ is 10

| 10 |

6 $\frac{1}{12}$ of ☐ is 12

| 12 |

7 $\frac{1}{12}$ of ☐ is 9

| 9 |

8 $\frac{1}{12}$ of ☐ is 6

| 6 |

9 $\frac{1}{12}$ of ☐ is 2

10 $\frac{1}{12}$ of ☐ is 5

11 $\frac{1}{12}$ of ☐ is 25

12 $\frac{1}{12}$ of ☐ is 20

13 $\frac{1}{12}$ of ☐ is 50

14 $\frac{1}{12}$ of ☐ is 70

15 $\frac{1}{12}$ of ☐ is 40

16 $\frac{1}{12}$ of ☐ is 30

17 $\frac{1}{12}$ of ☐ is 80

18 $\frac{1}{12}$ of ☐ is 90

Find $\frac{1}{12}$ of the numbers below by dividing them by 12.

Example $\frac{1}{12}$ of 72 = 6

6	6	6	6	6	6	6	6	6	6	6	6
72											

1 $\frac{1}{12}$ of 120 = ☐

2 $\frac{1}{12}$ of 48 = ☐

3 $\frac{1}{12}$ of 84 = ☐

4 $\frac{1}{12}$ of 144 = ☐

5 $\frac{1}{12}$ of 12 = ☐

6 $\frac{1}{12}$ of 24 = ☐

7 $\frac{1}{12}$ of 96 = ☐

8 $\frac{1}{12}$ of 60 = ☐

9 $\frac{1}{12}$ of 108 = ☐

10 $\frac{1}{12}$ of 132 = ☐

11 $\frac{1}{12}$ of 36 = ☐

12 $\frac{1}{12}$ of 360 = ☐

13 $\frac{1}{12}$ of 480 = ☐

14 $\frac{1}{12}$ of 840 = ☐

15 $\frac{1}{12}$ of 1,080 = ☐

16 $\frac{1}{12}$ of 1,440 = ☐

17 $\frac{1}{12}$ of 600 = ☐

18 $\frac{1}{12}$ of 240 = ☐

12 TIMES TABLE

Adjust these ingredients lists by the amounts shown. Use the number facts if you need to.

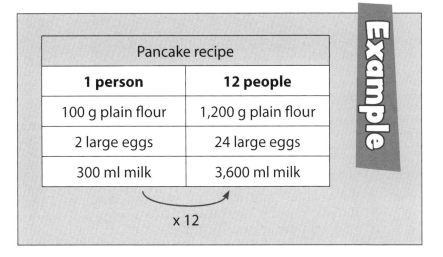

Example

Pancake recipe	
1 person	**12 people**
100 g plain flour	1,200 g plain flour
2 large eggs	24 large eggs
300 ml milk	3,600 ml milk

x 12

Multiply or divide each ingredient by the same number to scale the recipe up or down.

1

Milkshake recipe	
2 people	**24 people**
300 ml milk	
3 bananas	
2 chocolate bars	

x 12

2

Flapjack recipe	
1 flapjack traybake	**12 flapjack traybakes**
200 g oats	
120 g butter	
110 g brown sugar	

x 12

3

Fudge recipe	
60 pieces	**5 pieces**
480 g sugar	
600 ml cream	
360 g butter	

÷ 12

4

Rock cakes recipe	
36 rock cakes	**3 rock cakes**
240 g flour	
120 g sugar	
360 g butter	
72 g dried fruit	

÷ 12

5

Smoothie recipe	
1 smoothie	**12 smoothies**
11 strawberries	
9 cherries	
50 ml yoghurt	
100 ml juice	

x 12

Calculations

Use this space for jottings and written calculations.

Find the perimeters of these regular polygons (not drawn to scale).

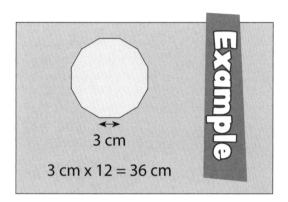

Example

3 cm

3 cm x 12 = 36 cm

Multiply the length of one side by the number of sides to find the perimeter of regular polygons.

1

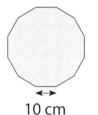

10 cm

Answer:

2

12 cm

Answer:

3

4 cm

Answer:

4

11 cm

Answer:

5

8 cm

Answer:

6

9 cm

Answer:

7

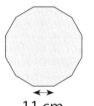

12 cm

Answer:

8

12 cm

Answer:

9

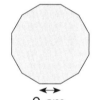

12 cm

Answer:

10

120 cm

Answer:

11

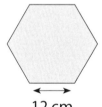

120 cm

Answer:

12

120 cm

Answer:

1 MIXED TABLES

Fill in the missing numbers.

Set 1

	x	9	=	9
11	x		=	44
54	=	9	x	
	=	35	÷	7
8	x		=	56
72	=		x	6
9	=	72	÷	
	=	7	x	4
8	x		=	16
99	÷	9	=	

Set 2

	÷	2	=	1
6	=	18	÷	
	x	5	=	40
54	=		x	6
3	x	10	=	
6	=		÷	9
	x	12	=	48
50	=	10	x	
	÷	4	=	3
10	÷	2	=	

Set 3

90	=	10	x	
	=	8	x	9
84	=	7	x	
	=	11	x	8
11	x	12	=	
	÷	12	=	9
96	=		x	8
4	x	6	=	
	=	7	x	3
6	÷	3	=	

Set 4

27	÷	9	=	
22	÷		=	11
3	x	6	=	
	=	3	x	9
5	x	4	=	
	=	81	÷	9
16	=	4	x	
	x	8	=	88
	x	8	=	32
24	÷	2	=	

Set 5

	=	99	÷	9
8	x	3	=	
4	=		÷	6
11	x	10	=	
30	÷		=	3
8	x	6	=	
	=	12	x	12
	=	12	x	3
49	=		x	7
12	=	108	÷	

Set 6

2	x		=	4
6	x	4	=	
40	=		x	5
12	x	5	=	
132	=		x	12
60	÷		=	5
12	=	72	÷	
	÷	10	=	6
20	=		x	4
12	=	36	÷	

Set 7

	=	10	÷	2
5	x		=	20
77	=		x	11
7	x	7	=	
11	x		=	55
5	x	6	=	
	=	30	÷	5
16	=		x	4
	÷	3	=	9
8	x	9	=	

Set 8

99	÷	11	=	
3	x		=	12
	=	3	x	6
24	=	4	x	
	=	2	x	12
32	÷		=	4
56	÷	8	=	
	x	5	=	60
32	÷		=	8
21	÷	3	=	

Set 9

72	÷	9	=	
	=	4	x	5
24	÷		=	4
8	x	8	=	
	÷	10	=	6
100	÷		=	10
8	=	72	÷	
	=	7	x	3
24	=		x	2
5	x	2	=	

Use all your times tables knowledge to find these equivalent fractions.

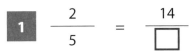

Example

$$\frac{12}{60} = \frac{1}{5}$$ (÷ 12, ÷ 12)

$$\frac{1}{5} = \frac{9}{45}$$ (x 9, x 9)

Multiply or divide the numerator and the denominator by the same number.

1. $\frac{2}{5} = \frac{14}{\Box}$

2. $\frac{42}{54} = \frac{\Box}{9}$

3. $\frac{2}{7} = \frac{18}{\Box}$

4. $\frac{\Box}{108} = \frac{11}{12}$

5. $\frac{4}{16} = \frac{2}{\Box}$

6. $\frac{18}{21} = \frac{\Box}{7}$

7. $\frac{\Box}{121} = \frac{3}{11}$

8. $\frac{4}{\Box} = \frac{32}{72}$

9. $\frac{3}{11} = \frac{15}{\Box}$

10. $\frac{\Box}{96} = \frac{1}{8}$

11. $\frac{\Box}{66} = \frac{4}{11}$

12. $\frac{1}{6} = \frac{3}{\Box}$

13. $\frac{2}{11} = \frac{4}{\Box}$

14. $\frac{70}{80} = \frac{\Box}{8}$

15. $\frac{9}{45} = \frac{1}{\Box}$

16. $\frac{6}{11} = \frac{\Box}{99}$

17. $\frac{11}{12} = \frac{44}{\Box}$

18. $\frac{4}{7} = \frac{\Box}{56}$

19. $\frac{\Box}{11} = \frac{32}{44}$

20. $\frac{\Box}{42} = \frac{5}{6}$

21. $\frac{110}{121} = \frac{10}{\Box}$

22. $\frac{5}{9} = \frac{\Box}{72}$

1 Calculate the area of each of these rectangles (not drawn to scale).

Example

12 cm

24 cm²

2 cm

12 cm x 2 cm = 24 cm²

a 10 cm / 8 cm

b 8 cm / 4 cm

c 7 cm / 2 cm

d 4 cm / 11 cm

e 7 cm / 7 cm

f 12 cm / 7 cm

g 5 cm / 2 cm

h 9 cm / 3 cm

i 4 cm / 9 cm

j 12 cm / 8 cm

k 3 cm / 8 cm

l 12 cm / 6 cm

m 7 cm / 8 cm

2 Find the area of rectangles with these measurements.

Ninja Challenge

a	40 cm long and 60 cm wide	
b	30 cm long and 110 cm wide	
c	20 cm long and 90 cm wide	

Write the multiplication or division calculation and answer for each of these word problems.

1	A teacher puts 32 children equally into 4 groups. How many children will there be in each group?	
2	There are 12 pairs of socks in a drawer. How many socks are there in total?	
3	A shelf can hold 12 books. If Maisie has 132 books, how many shelves will she need?	
4	If there are 7 spiders in a tank, how many legs will there be altogether?	
5	Eggs come in boxes of 8. If there are 3 boxes on a shelf, how many eggs will there be altogether?	
6	A type of flower has 5 petals. How many petals will 9 identical flowers have?	
7	3 children equally share 18 biscuits between themselves. How many will they get each?	
8	In a box of biscuits, there are 3 layers, which each contain 12 biscuits. How many biscuits will there be in total?	
9	There are 110 sweets in a bag. If 11 children share them equally, how many will they get each?	
10	A bicycle has 2 wheels. How many wheels will 90 bicycles have altogether?	
11	A set of twins share 80 grapes equally. How many grapes will they receive each?	
12	A TV show has 30 episodes in each season. How many episodes will there be in 11 seasons?	
13	Pens come in packs of 6. If there are 80 packs, how many pens will there be in total?	
14	If shelves can hold 30 books, how many shelves will be needed to hold 1,440 books?	

Adjust these ingredients lists by the amounts shown. Use the number facts if you need to.

1 Hot chocolate recipe

1 hot chocolate	2 hot chocolates	5 hot chocolates	11 hot chocolates
200 ml milk			
30 g chocolate			
2 teaspoons cocoa			

2 Smoothie recipe

1 smoothie	3 smoothies	12 smoothies	6 smoothies
100 ml milk			
60 ml yoghurt			
7 strawberries			
12 blackcurrants			

3 Biscuit recipe

10 biscuits	40 biscuits	70 biscuits	90 biscuits
100 g butter			
50 g sugar			
120 g flour			
2 teaspoons cocoa			

4 Yorkshire pudding recipe

10 puddings	80 puddings	60 puddings	90 puddings
120 g flour			
4 eggs			
200 ml milk			
2 teaspoons oil			

Find the fractions of the numbers below using all the times tables.

Example

$$\frac{7}{9} \text{ of } 45 \text{ is } \boxed{35}$$

$$45 \div 9 = 5$$

$$5 \times 7 = 35$$

> Divide the number by the denominator, then multiply that answer by the numerator.

1 $\frac{7}{8}$ of 72 = ☐

2 $\frac{3}{4}$ of 48 = ☐

3 $\frac{2}{3}$ of 12 = ☐

4 $\frac{5}{6}$ of 42 = ☐

5 $\frac{8}{11}$ of 99 = ☐

6 $\frac{3}{5}$ of 35 = ☐

7 $\frac{4}{9}$ of 63 = ☐

8 $\frac{2}{9}$ of 54 = ☐

9 $\frac{7}{9}$ of 99 = ☐

10 $\frac{3}{8}$ of 48 = ☐

11 $\frac{2}{7}$ of 42 = ☐

12 $\frac{11}{12}$ of 72 = ☐

13 $\frac{4}{9}$ of 18 = ☐

14 $\frac{4}{5}$ of 60 = ☐

15 $\frac{3}{8}$ of 56 = ☐

16 $\frac{2}{11}$ of 88 = ☐

17 $\frac{4}{9}$ of 45 = ☐

18 $\frac{5}{8}$ of 56 = ☐

Calculations

Use this space for jottings and written calculations.

Complete these short division questions using all the tables.

Example

$732 \div 2 = 366$

```
        3    6    6
2 | 7   ¹3   ¹2
```

You could write out the times table to help you with these questions.

1
```
4 | 9   4   0
```

2
```
8 | 6   8   8
```

3
```
7 | 5   5   3
```

4
```
9 | 6   9   3
```

5
```
5 | 7   2   5
```

6
```
11 | 7   4   8
```

7
```
2 | 9   9   6
```

8
```
12 | 9   3   6
```

9
```
9 | 2   2   9   5
```

10	1,278	÷	6	=
11	996	÷	4	=
12	1,280	÷	5	=
13	894	÷	3	=

14	992	÷	8	=
15	672	÷	7	=
16	1,026	÷	9	=
17	1,794	÷	3	=

Calculations

Use this space for jottings and written calculations.

8

Find the perimeters of these regular polygons (not drawn to scale).

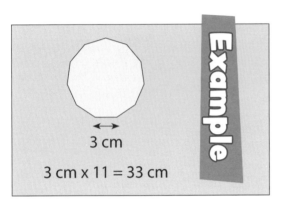

Example

3 cm

3 cm x 11 = 33 cm

Multiply the length of one side by the number of sides to find the perimeter of regular polygons.

1 2 3 4 5 6 7 8 9 0

1

10 cm

Answer:

2

12 cm

Answer:

3

3 cm

Answer:

4

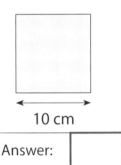

6 cm

Answer:

5

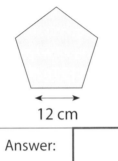

8 cm

Answer:

6

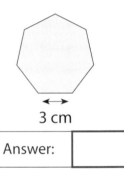

6 cm

Answer:

7

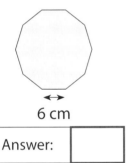

11 cm

Answer:

8

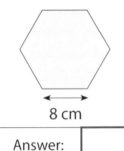

4 cm

Answer:

9

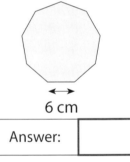

8 cm

Answer:

10

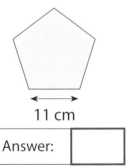

8 cm

Answer:

11

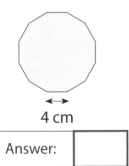

5 cm

Answer:

12

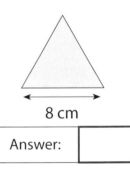

3 cm

Answer:

Use your known times table facts to solve these multiplication and division problems.

Example

5 x 4 = 20

5 x 40 = 200

#	Problem	Answer		#	Problem	Answer
1	600 x 4 =			16	8,000 x 3 =	
2	7 x 60 =			17	60 x 50 =	
3	40 x 90 =			18	900 x 5 =	
4	4,000 ÷ 8 =			19	4 x 800 =	
5	80 x 70 =			20	900 ÷ 3 =	
6	120 x 6 =			21	1,200 x 7 =	
7	900 x 7 =			22	500 x 800 =	
8	9 x 600 =			23	5,600 ÷ 8 =	
9	180 ÷ 6 =			24	600 x 90 =	
10	4,400 ÷ 11 =			25	500 x 7 =	
11	800 x 60 =			26	3,200 ÷ 8 =	
12	700 x 2 =			27	80 x 30 =	
13	5 x 70 =			28	12 x 80 =	
14	240 ÷ 8 =			29	900 x 8 =	
15	700 x 9 =			30	540 ÷ 9 =	

Calculations

Use this space for jottings and written calculations.

Use the given fraction to find the whole number.

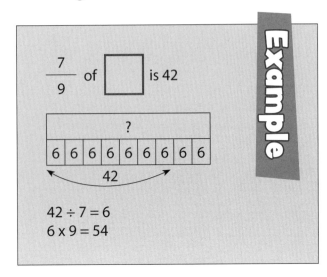

Example

$\frac{7}{9}$ of ☐ is 42

| ? |
| 6 | 6 | 6 | 6 | 6 | 6 | 6 | 6 | 6 |

42

$42 \div 7 = 6$
$6 \times 9 = 54$

Divide the number by the numerator, then multiply that answer by the denominator to find the whole number.

1 $\frac{6}{8}$ of ☐ is 48

2 $\frac{4}{5}$ of ☐ is 36

3 $\frac{6}{10}$ of ☐ is 24

4 $\frac{3}{7}$ of ☐ is 18

5 $\frac{9}{11}$ of ☐ is 81

6 $\frac{8}{9}$ of ☐ is 80

7 $\frac{7}{12}$ of ☐ is 77

8 $\frac{3}{4}$ of ☐ is 18

9 $\frac{6}{10}$ of ☐ is 72

10 $\frac{2}{3}$ of ☐ is 14

11 $\frac{2}{5}$ of ☐ is 16

12 $\frac{4}{11}$ of ☐ is 44

13 $\frac{7}{9}$ of ☐ is 56

14 $\frac{2}{9}$ of ☐ is 20

15 $\frac{4}{12}$ of ☐ is 24

16 $\frac{6}{7}$ of ☐ is 36

17 $\frac{2}{11}$ of ☐ is 16

18 $\frac{4}{9}$ of ☐ is 32

Complete these short multiplication questions using your times table knowledge.

Example	574 x 4	
500 x 4	2,000
70 x 4	280
4 x 4	16
Total:	2,296

1	874 x 9	
800 x 9	
70 x 9	
4 x 9	
Total:	

2	683 x 4	
600 x 4	
80 x 4	
3 x 4	
Total:	

3	582 x 3	
500 x 3	
80 x 3	
2 x 3	
Total:	

4	245 x 7	
200 x 7	
40 x 7	
5 x 7	
Total:	

5	327 x 5	
300 x 5	
20 x 5	
7 x 5	
Total:	

6	563 x 9	
500 x 9	
60 x 9	
3 x 9	
Total:	

7	753 x 8	
700 x 8	
50 x 8	
3 x 8	
Total:	

8	764 x 6	
700 x 6	
60 x 6	
4 x 6	
Total:	

9	593	x	4	=
10	695	x	7	=

11	647	x	8	=
12	452	x	9	=

Calculations

Use this space for jottings and written calculations.

Find the areas of these triangles by multiplying the base by the height and then dividing the answer by 2 (not drawn to scale).

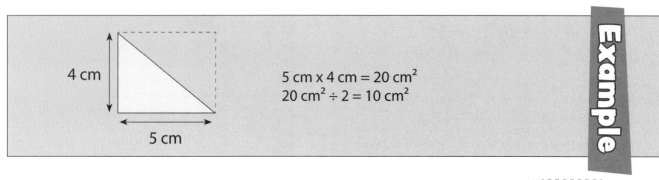

Example

4 cm

5 cm

5 cm x 4 cm = 20 cm²
20 cm² ÷ 2 = 10 cm²

1

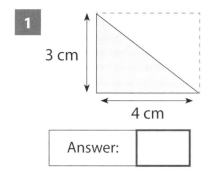

3 cm

4 cm

Answer:

2

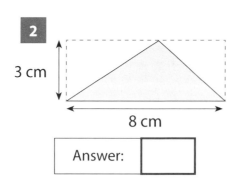

3 cm

8 cm

Answer:

3

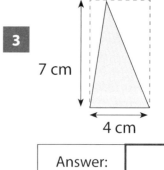

7 cm

4 cm

Answer:

4

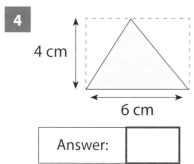

4 cm

6 cm

Answer:

5

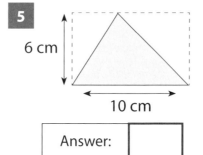

6 cm

10 cm

Answer:

6

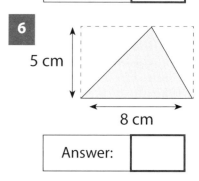

5 cm

8 cm

Answer:

7

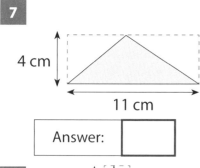

4 cm

11 cm

Answer:

8

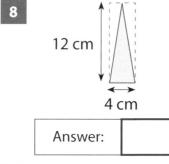

12 cm

4 cm

Answer:

9

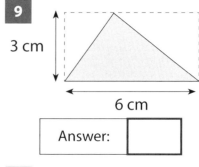

3 cm

6 cm

Answer:

10

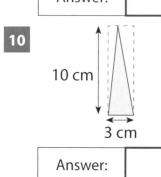

10 cm

3 cm

Answer:

11

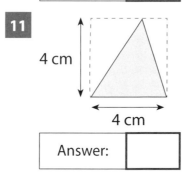

4 cm

4 cm

Answer:

12

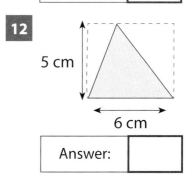

5 cm

6 cm

Answer:

CONGRATULATIONS!

You have mastered the

times table!

CONGRATULATIONS!

You are a Times Tables Ninja!

2 times table

1

1

1	2	3	4	5	6	7	8	9	10
11	12	13	14	15	16	17	18	19	20
21	22	23	24	25	26	27	28	29	30
31	32	33	34	35	36	37	38	39	40
41	42	43	44	45	46	47	48	49	50
51	52	53	54	55	56	57	58	59	60
61	62	63	64	65	66	67	68	69	70
71	72	73	74	75	76	77	78	79	80
81	82	83	84	85	86	87	88	89	90
91	92	93	94	95	96	97	98	99	100

2

2	x	2	=	4	2	5	x	2	=	10	16	3
12	13	x	2	x	3	10	9	2	x	2	x	9
10	x	2	4	2	=	4	x	x	3	=	2	3
x	14	=	2	=	8	x	2	4	x	20	=	x
2	X	2	=	8	x	2	=	16	2	22	8	2
=	6	4	6	16	6	12	18	x	=	14	6	=
20	11	x	4	x	2	x	6	=	7	22	24	6
6	1	x	2	=	2	6	2	11	x	=	7	x
8	x	2	=	20	4	=	2	=	8	2	x	2
12	x	2	=	24	18	x	12	3	9	x	6	16
10	x	2	7	x	2	=	14	x	=	11	24	2

2

Set 1	Set 2	Set 3	Set 4	Set 5	Set 6	Set 7	Set 8	Set 9
3 x 2 = **6**	**8 ÷ 2 = 4**	**9** x 2 = 18	4 ÷ 2 = **2**	11 x 2 = **22**	**16** ÷ 2 = 8	**22** ÷ 2 = 11	**8** = 16 ÷ 2	**4** = 2 x 2
6 x 2 = 12	**4** x 2 = 8	16 ÷ 2 = **8**	**6** ÷ 2 = 3	12 x 2 = **24**	18 ÷ 2 = **9**	16 = **8** x 2	9 = **18** ÷ 2	6 = **3** x 2
7 x 2 = 14	5 x 2 = **10**	18 ÷ 2 = **9**	1 x 2 = **2**	**12** ÷ 2 = 6	**20** ÷ 2 = 10	**18** = 9 x 2	10 = **20** ÷ 2	1 = **2** ÷ 2
10 x 2 = 20	8 x 2 = **16**	**20** ÷ 2 = 10	10 x 2 = **20**	**22** ÷ 2 = 11	10 ÷ 2 = **5**	**20** = 10 x 2	11 = **22** ÷ 2	7 x 2 = 14
2 ÷ 2 = **1**	**9** x 2 = 18	**22** ÷ 2 = 11	**2** ÷ 2 = 1	**24** ÷ 2 = 12	**2** = 4 ÷ 2	22 = **11** x 2	11 x 2 = 22	**14** ÷ 2 = 7
10 ÷ 2 = 5	**16** ÷ 2 = 8	24 ÷ 2 = **12**	**2** x 2 = 8	3 x 2 = **6**	3 = **6** ÷ 2	4 x 2 = **8**	24 = **12** x 2	**5** = 10 ÷ 2
11 x 2 = **22**	18 ÷ 2 = **9**	**4** ÷ 2 = 2	16 ÷ 2 = **8**	6 x 2 = **12**	**4** = 8 ÷ 2	8 = **4** x 2	**5** x 2 = 10	**6** = 12 ÷ 2
12 x 2 = **24**	**20** ÷ 2 = 10	**6** ÷ 2 = 3	18 ÷ 2 = **9**	**7** x 2 = 14	24 ÷ 2 = **12**	10 = **5** x 2	8 x 2 = **16**	7 = **14** ÷ 2
12 ÷ 2 = 6	22 ÷ 2 = **11**	1 x 2 = **2**	**20** ÷ 2 = 10	14 ÷ 2 = **7**	**3** x 2 = 6	**12** = 6 x 2	9 x 2 = 18	**8** ÷ 2 = 4
14 ÷ 2 = **7**	24 ÷ 2 = **12**	2 x 2 = **4**	10 ÷ 2 = **5**	8 ÷ 2 = **4**	6 x 2 = **12**	14 = **7** x 2	2 = **1** x 2	12 = **24** ÷ 2

3

1

2	1	5	7	23	15	17	24	26	27	25	24	21
8	9	8	7	13	12	19	21	22	24	23	21	28
6	10	12	21	23	5	7	1	2	7	3	6	8
1	3	20	6	11	16	13	21	9	19	15	22	12
17	15	22	25	23	1	7	11	24	1	3	17	10
19	12	24	15	17	19	21	14	18	24	22	18	23
13	11	2	16	18	5	7	12	21	13	3	14	3
15	18	21	11	14	12	8	10	17	1	2	12	5
12	22	25	15	17	21	22	17	19	5	22	16	13
17	4	5	7	19	13	10	16	17	21	23	2	15
2	6	12	13	4	17	23	19	8	1	5	4	exit

2

a	2 + 2 + 2 + 2 + 2 + 2	6 x 2	12
b	**2**	1 x 2	2
c	2 + 2 + 2 + 2 + 2	5 x 2	**10**
d	2 + 2	**2 x 2**	4
e	**2 + 2 + 2 + 2 + 2 + 2 + 2 + 2 + 2 + 2 + 2**	11 x 2	22
f	2 + 2 + 2 + 2 + 2 + 2 + 2 + 2	**8 x 2**	16
g	2 + 2 + 2 + 2	4 x 2	**8**
h	2 + 2 + 2 + 2 + 2 + 2 + 2 + 2 + 2 + 2 + 2 + 2	12 x 2	**24**
i	**2 + 2 + 2 + 2 + 2 + 2 + 2 + 2 + 2 + 2**	10 x 2	20
j	2 + 2 + 2	**3 x 2**	6
k	2 + 2 + 2 + 2 + 2 + 2 + 2 + 2 + 2	9 x 2	**18**
l	2 + 2 + 2 + 2 + 2 + 2 + 2	**7 x 2**	14

4

1

a 2 cm²
b 4 cm²
c 6 cm²
d 10 cm²
e 12 cm²
f 20 cm²
g 14 cm²
h 22 cm²
i 18 cm²
j 8 cm²
k 16 cm²

2

a 100 cm²
b 600 cm²
c 40 cm²

5

1

a 4, 40, 400
b 6, 60, 600
c 8, 80, 800
d 10, 100, 1,000
e 12, 120, 1,200
f 14, 140, 1,400
g 16, 160, 1,600
h 18, 180, 1,800
i 20, 200, 2,000
j 22, 220, 2,200
k 24, 240, 2,400

2

a 56
b 150
c 78
d 114
e 96
f 568
g 944
h 790

6

1 161
2 131
3 231
4 62
5 164
6 430
7 369
8 107
9 116
10 336
11 211
12 183
13 1,116
14 1,732
15 821
16 1,316
17 3,383

7

1 8 x 2 = 16
2 12 ÷ 2 = 6
3 11 x 2 = 22
4 6 x 2 = 12
5 12 x 2 = 24
6 8 ÷ 2 = 4
7 6 x 2 = 12
8 10 x 2 = 20
9 6 ÷ 2 = 3
10 120 ÷ 2 = 60
11 £80 ÷ 2 = £40
12 £30 x 2 = £60
13 25 x 2 = 50
14 16 x 2 = 32

8

1 $\dfrac{2}{\mathbf{5}} = \dfrac{4}{10}$

2 $\dfrac{14}{18} = \dfrac{\mathbf{7}}{9}$

3 $\dfrac{2}{7} = \dfrac{\mathbf{4}}{14}$

4 $\dfrac{22}{24} = \dfrac{11}{\mathbf{12}}$

5 $\dfrac{10}{\mathbf{16}} = \dfrac{5}{8}$

6 $\dfrac{\mathbf{12}}{14} = \dfrac{6}{7}$

7 $\dfrac{6}{22} = \dfrac{\mathbf{3}}{11}$

8 $\dfrac{10}{20} = \dfrac{20}{\mathbf{40}}$

9 $\dfrac{8}{11} = \dfrac{\mathbf{16}}{22}$

10 $\dfrac{6}{\mathbf{40}} = \dfrac{3}{20}$

11 $\dfrac{\mathbf{20}}{66} = \dfrac{10}{33}$

12 $\dfrac{3}{15} = \dfrac{6}{\mathbf{30}}$

13 $\dfrac{2}{11} = \dfrac{\mathbf{4}}{22}$

14 $\dfrac{14}{16} = \dfrac{7}{\mathbf{8}}$

15 $\dfrac{8}{24} = \dfrac{4}{\mathbf{12}}$

16 $\dfrac{15}{16} = \dfrac{30}{\mathbf{32}}$

17 $\dfrac{24}{30} = \dfrac{\mathbf{48}}{60}$

18 $\dfrac{10}{12} = \dfrac{20}{\mathbf{24}}$

19 $\dfrac{2}{11} = \dfrac{\mathbf{4}}{22}$

20 $\dfrac{18}{30} = \dfrac{\mathbf{9}}{15}$

21 $\dfrac{50}{60} = \dfrac{25}{\mathbf{30}}$

22 $\dfrac{4}{6} = \dfrac{\mathbf{8}}{12}$

9

1 16
2 10
3 8
4 6
5 4
6 22
7 20
8 12
9 24
10 18
11 26
12 40
13 100
14 50
15 120
16 90
17 46
18 800

10

1 10
2 1
3 8
4 2
5 4
6 11
7 9
8 3
9 12
10 7
11 6
12 13
13 100
14 120
15 40
16 16
17 24
18 300

11

1 400 ml milk, 6 bananas, 4 chocolate bars
2 400 g oats, 240 g butter, 220g brown sugar
3 200 g sugar, 150 ml cream, 25 g butter
4 110 g flour, 40 g sugar, 60 g butter, 80 g dried fruit
5 22 strawberries, 18 cherries, 100 ml yoghurt, 200 ml juice

12

1 2 cm x 6 = 12 cm
2 2 cm x 5 = 10 cm
3 2 cm x 4 = 8 cm
4 2 cm x 8 = 16 cm
5 2 cm x 9 = 18 cm
6 2 cm x 12 = 24 cm
7 2 cm x 10 = 20 cm
8 20 cm x 11 = 22 cm
9 20 cm x 6 = 120 cm
10 20 cm x 5 = 100 cm
11 20 cm x 8 = 160 cm
12 20 cm x 9 = 180 cm

3 times table

1

1

1	2	3	4	5	6	7	8	9	10
11	12	13	14	15	16	17	18	19	20
21	22	23	24	25	26	27	28	29	30
31	32	33	34	35	36	37	38	39	40
41	42	43	44	45	46	47	48	49	50
51	52	53	54	55	56	57	58	59	60
61	62	63	64	65	66	67	68	69	70
71	72	73	74	75	76	77	78	79	80
81	82	83	84	85	86	87	88	89	90
91	92	93	94	95	96	97	98	99	100

2

1	x	3	=	3	6	7	8	x	3	=	24	6
4	x	3	=	16	x	x	x	11	x	3	3	9
11	x	3	=	36	24	3	3	3	9	12	x	x
9	5	x	3	10	x	3	=	30	=	15	3	3
11	x	3	=	33	18	36	4	9	8	14	=	=
12	12	3	x	5	x	4	18	x	8	2	6	27
2	9	x	4	x	3	=	12	3	7	x	3	7
x	9	12	3	3	3	x	3	=	x	3	3	x
3	36	x	9	=	24	27	33	30	3	=	18	=
=	33	8	3	15	36	6	x	3	=	18	27	24
6	12	x	3	=	4	x	3	=	21	30	33	3

2

Set 1	Set 2	Set 3	Set 4	Set 5	Set 6	Set 7	Set 8	Set 9
7 x 3 = **21**	36 ÷ 3 = **12**	**11** x 3 = 33	**2** x 3 = 6	24 = **8** x 3	5 x 3 = **15**	**27** ÷ 3 = 9	15 ÷ 3 = **5**	4 = **12** ÷ 3
18 = 6 x 3	**9** ÷ 3 = 3	**30** = 10 x 3	3 x 3 = **9**	**27** = 9 x 3	**8** x 3 = 24	30 ÷ 3 = **10**	**3** = 9 ÷ 3	**12** x 3 = 36
21 = 7 x 3	2 = **6** ÷ 3	33 = **11** x 3	**9** x 3 = 27	9 = **3** x 3	36 = **12** x 3	**33** ÷ 3 = 11	**11** x 3 = 33	3 = **1** x 3
6 ÷ 3 = 2	**3** = 9 ÷ 3	**2** x 3 = 6	**9** ÷ 3 = 3	**12** x 3 = 36	**3** ÷ 3 = 1	36 ÷ 3 = **12**	27 = **9** x 3	**6** = 2 x 3
12 = **4** x 3	4 = **12** ÷ 3	3 x 3 = **9**	1 x 3 = **3**	3 = **1** x 3	**4** = 12 ÷ 3	**1** = 3 ÷ 3	**24** ÷ 3 = 8	9 = **27** ÷ 3
15 = 5 x 3	5 = **15** ÷ 3	**12** x 3 = 36	**11** = 33 ÷ 3	6 = **2** x 3	5 = **15** ÷ 3	2 = **6** ÷ 3	24 = **8** x 3	**10** = 30 ÷ 3
6 x 3 = **18**	**6** = 18 ÷ 3	**3** = 1 x 3	12 = **36** ÷ 3	**9** = 27 ÷ 3	6 = **18** ÷ 3	3 = **9** ÷ 3	4 x 3 = **12**	**30** = 10 x 3
27 ÷ 3 = **9**	**7** = 21 ÷ 3	6 = **2** x 3	**12** ÷ 3 = 4	10 = **30** ÷ 3	**7** = 21 ÷ 3	11 x 3 = **33**	**5** x 3 = 15	33 = **11** x 3
30 ÷ 3 = 10	8 = **24** ÷ 3	**9** = 27 ÷ 3	**15** ÷ 3 = 5	**4** x 3 = 12	8 = **24** ÷ 3	**30** = 10 x 3	8 x 3 = **24**	**2** x 3 = 6
33 ÷ 3 = **11**	10 x 3 = **30**	10 = **30** ÷ 3	18 ÷ 3 = **6**	5 x 3 = **15**	10 x 3 = **30**	33 = **11** x 3		21 ÷ 3 = **7**

3

1

3	6	9	1	22	31	5	24	9	7	9	1	2
22	1	12	22	16	15	26	3	8	22	3	4	18
26	19	33	31	35	3	6	21	24	29	28	11	22
29	15	36	18	12	15	7	8	18	30	33	19	16
32	4	17	29	6	13	8	3	13	19	36	22	17
23	7	15	8	21	11	12	19	22	22	6	36	10
32	2	19	9	29	16	19	22	16	34	9	17	12
21	17	28	2	25	22	20	18	13	15	12	19	17
31	23	36	6	19	17	22	15	9	21	23	27	22
17	6	27	8	13	10	25	4	2	18	22	29	28
18	8	23	1	12	19	27	1	11	24	36	9	exit

2

a	3 + 3	1 x 3	3
b	**3 + 3 + 3 + 3 + 3 + 3**	6 x 3	18
c	3 + 3 + 3 + 3 + 3 + 3 + 3 + 3	**8 x 3**	**24**
d	**3 + 3 + 3 + 3 + 3 + 3 + 3 + 3 + 3 + 3 + 3 + 3**	**12 x 3**	36
e	3 + 3	**2 x 3**	6
f	**3 + 3 + 3 + 3 + 3**	5 x 3	**15**
g	**3 + 3 + 3 + 3 + 3 + 3 + 3 + 3 + 3 + 3 + 3**	**11 x 3**	33
h	3 + 3 + 3 + 3 + 3 + 3 + 3	7 x 3	**21**
i	**3 + 3 + 3**	3 x 3	9
j	3 + 3 + 3 + 3 + 3 + 3 + 3 + 3 + 3 + 3	10 x 3	**30**
k	**3 + 3 + 3 + 3**	**4 x 3**	12
l	3 + 3 + 3 + 3 + 3 + 3 + 3 + 3 + 3	**9 x 3**	27

4

1

a $3\ cm^2$
b $36\ cm^2$
c $9\ cm^2$
d $15\ cm^2$
e $12\ cm^2$
f $27\ cm^2$
g $30\ cm^2$
h $21\ cm^2$
i $18\ cm^2$
j $24\ cm^2$
k $33\ cm^2$

2

a $150\ cm^2$
b $360\ cm^2$
c $120\ cm^2$

5

1

a 6, 60, 600
b 9, 90, 900
c 12, 120, 1,200
d 15, 150, 1,500
e 18, 180, 1,800
f 21, 210, 2,100
g 24, 240, 2,400
h 27, 270, 2,700
i 30, 300, 3,000
j 33, 330, 3,300
k 36, 360, 3,600

2

a 84
b 225
c 117
d 171
e 144
f 852
g 1,416
h 1,185

6

1 265
2 135
3 253
4 231
5 241
6 276
7 235
8 251
9 243
10 334
11 86
12 124
13 78
14 356
15 586
16 546
17 856

7

1 8 x 3 = 24
2 12 x 3 = 36
3 9 ÷ 3 = 3
4 18 ÷ 3 = 6
5 £11 x 3 = £33
6 2 x 3 = 6
7 9 x 3 = 27
8 10 x 3 = 30
9 £24 ÷ 3 = £8
10 120 ÷ 3 = 40
11 £120 x 3 = £360
12 180 ÷ 3 = 60
13 30 x 3 = 90
14 240 ÷ 3 = 80

8

1 $\dfrac{2}{5} = \dfrac{6}{15}$

2 $\dfrac{21}{24} = \dfrac{7}{8}$

3 $\dfrac{2}{7} = \dfrac{6}{21}$

4 $\dfrac{33}{36} = \dfrac{11}{12}$

5 $\dfrac{12}{15} = \dfrac{4}{5}$

6 $\dfrac{18}{21} = \dfrac{6}{7}$

7 $\dfrac{9}{33} = \dfrac{3}{11}$

8 $\dfrac{7}{8} = \dfrac{21}{24}$

9 $\dfrac{5}{12} = \dfrac{15}{36}$

10 $\dfrac{9}{33} = \dfrac{3}{11}$

11 $\dfrac{21}{33} = \dfrac{7}{11}$

12 $\dfrac{2}{10} = \dfrac{6}{30}$

13 $\dfrac{2}{11} = \dfrac{6}{33}$

14 $\dfrac{12}{27} = \dfrac{4}{9}$

15 $\dfrac{6}{24} = \dfrac{2}{8}$

16 $\dfrac{10}{11} = \dfrac{30}{33}$

17 $\dfrac{4}{12} = \dfrac{12}{36}$

18 $\dfrac{4}{7} = \dfrac{12}{21}$

19 $\dfrac{8}{11} = \dfrac{24}{33}$

20 $\dfrac{15}{30} = \dfrac{5}{10}$

21 $\dfrac{30}{36} = \dfrac{10}{12}$

22 $\dfrac{5}{7} = \dfrac{15}{21}$

9

1 24
2 15
3 12
4 9
5 6
6 33
7 30
8 18
9 36
10 27
11 39
12 60
13 150
14 75
15 45
16 66
17 180
18 90

10

1 1
2 7
3 2
4 5
5 11
6 12
7 3
8 8
9 6
10 9
11 4
12 120
13 80
14 30
15 33
16 60
17 40
18 200

11

1 600 ml milk, 9 bananas, 6 chocolate bars
2 600 g oats, 360 g butter, 330 g brown sugar
3 100 g sugar, 120 ml cream, 40 g butter
4 45 g flour, 25 g sugar, 40 g butter, 60 g dried fruit
5 33 strawberries, 27 cherries, 150 ml yoghurt, 300 ml juice

12

1 10 cm x 3 = 30 cm
2 12 cm x 3 = 36 cm
3 4 cm x 3 = 12 cm
4 11 cm x 3 = 33 cm
5 8 cm x 3 = 24 cm
6 9 cm x 3 = 27 cm
7 3 cm x 6 = 18 cm
8 3 cm x 4 = 12 cm
9 30 cm x 5 = 150 cm
10 3 cm x 8 = 24 cm
11 30 cm x 7 = 210 cm
12 3 cm x 12 = 36 cm

4 times table

1

1

1	2	3	4	5	6	7	8	9	10
11	12	13	14	15	16	17	18	19	20
21	22	23	24	25	26	27	28	29	30
31	32	33	34	35	36	37	38	39	40
41	42	43	44	45	46	47	48	49	50
51	52	53	54	55	56	57	58	59	60
61	62	63	64	65	66	67	68	69	70
71	72	73	74	75	76	77	78	79	80
81	82	83	84	85	86	87	88	89	90
91	92	93	94	95	96	97	98	99	100

2

1	x	4	=	4	3	6	9	x	4	=	3	4
8	10	x	4	=	40	x	x	x	4	6	x	x
12	x	3	6	x	4	=	24	4	4	24	4	4
x	4	9	x	8	x	4	=	40	8	=	=	=
4	2	5	x	44	5	40	8	44	48	3	36	16
=	8	x	=	4	32	7	x	4	=	28	=	4
48	x	3	4	8	=	44	4	8	x	4	5	3
12	5	x	4	=	20	32	=	12	x	4	=	44
5	x	4	=	25	8	4	32	11	x	4	=	14
3	x	4	=	11	2	x	8	x	4	=	24	12
11	x	4	=	44	8	x	4	3	x	4	=	12

2

Set 1	Set 2	Set 3	Set 4	Set 5	Set 6	Set 7	Set 8	Set 9
1 x 4 = **4**	16 = **4** x 4	12 x 4 = **48**	48 = **12** x 4	**11** = 44 ÷ 4	10 = **40** ÷ 4	4 ÷ 4 = **1**	**8** ÷ 4 = 2	28 = **7** x 4
10 x 4 = 40	**36** = 9 x 4	**28** ÷ 4 = 7	**4** ÷ 4 = 1	12 = **48** ÷ 4	8 x 4 = **32**	**8** ÷ 4 = 2	3 = **12** ÷ 4	**32** = 8 x 4
11 x 4 = 44	**40** ÷ 4 = 10	10 = **40** ÷ 4	8 ÷ 4 = **2**	44 = **11** x 4	**9** x 4 = 36	3 = **12** ÷ 4	**8** = 2 x 4	2 = **8** ÷ 4
28 = **7** x 4	**4** x 4 = 16	**8** x 4 = 32	**3** = 12 ÷ 4	2 x 4 = **8**	44 ÷ 4 = **11**	**8** = 2 x 4	12 = **3** x 4	**36** ÷ 4 = 9
32 = 8 x 4	16 ÷ 4 = **4**	9 x 4 = **36**	**8** = 2 x 4	**6** x 4 = 24	**48** ÷ 4 = 12	12 = **3** x 4	3 x 4 = **12**	**24** ÷ 4 = 6
2 = **8** ÷ 4	**40** = 10 x 4	**44** ÷ 4 = 11	12 = **3** x 4	**20** = 5 x 4	36 ÷ 4 = **9**	**3** x 4 = 12	**32** ÷ 4 = 8	20 ÷ 4 = **5**
36 ÷ 4 = 9	**12** ÷ 4 = 3	48 ÷ 4 = **12**	3 x 4 = **12**	7 x 4 = **28**	**24** ÷ 4 = 6	32 ÷ 4 = **8**	**11** = 44 ÷ 4	**5** x 4 = 20
24 ÷ 4 = 6	**6** = 24 ÷ 4	**1** = 4 ÷ 4	**32** ÷ 4 = 8	**4** = 16 ÷ 4	**20** ÷ 4 = 5	**11** = 44 ÷ 4	12 = **48** ÷ 4	**16** = 4 x 4
20 ÷ 4 = **5**	**7** = 28 ÷ 4	**9** = 36 ÷ 4	11 = **44** ÷ 4	5 = **20** ÷ 4	5 x 4 = **20**	12 = **48** ÷ 4	**44** = 11 x 4	36 = **9** x 4
5 x 4 = **20**	8 = **32** ÷ 4	24 = **6** x 4	12 = **48** ÷ 4	4 = **1** x 4	**16** = 4 x 4	36 ÷ 4 = **9**	**2** x 4 = 8	**40** ÷ 4 = 10

3

1

4	1	8	14	26	37	48	45	18	2	29	4	14
12	5	18	12	26	32	36	24	16	25	6	24	45
16	7	25	36	37	34	21	11	17	15	19	27	22
8	17	36	25	38	14	31	25	26	32	35	21	18
32	10	21	22	41	16	42	31	42	34	29	31	40
36	19	7	22	23	12	16	18	21	13	9	25	28
44	23	12	36	48	4	5	26	16	18	19	20	23
48	18	15	32	33	8	25	38	15	18	22	18	6
12	16	20	24	38	12	26	13	7	40	44	11	22
20	34	26	29	30	16	34	38	8	36	27	30	7
42	48	36	24	9	32	40	44	48	16	12	32	exit

2

a	4 + 4 + 4 + 4 + 4 + 4	6 x 4	24
b	4 + 4	**2 x 4**	**8**
c	4 + 4 + 4 + 4 + 4 + 4 + 4 + 4 + 4 + 4 + 4	**11 x 4**	44
d	4 + 4 + 4 + 4 + 4 + 4 + 4	**7 x 4**	28
e	4	**1 x 4**	4
f	**4 + 4 + 4 + 4 + 4 + 4 + 4 + 4 + 4 + 4 + 4 + 4**	12 x 4	48
g	4 + 4 + 4 + 4 + 4 + 4 + 4 + 4	**8 x 4**	32
h	4 + 4 + 4 + 4 + 4	5 x 4	**20**
i	**4 + 4 + 4 + 4 + 4 + 4 + 4 + 4 + 4 + 4**	10 x 4	40
j	**4 + 4 + 4**	3 x 4	**12**
k	**4 + 4 + 4 + 4**	**4 x 4**	16
l	4 + 4 + 4 + 4 + 4 + 4 + 4 + 4 + 4	**9 x 4**	**36**

4

1

a   4 cm²
b   16 cm²
c   8 cm²
d   12 cm²
e   20 cm²
f   36 cm²
g   32 cm²
h   40 cm²
i   28 cm²
j   24 cm²
k   44 cm²

2

a   120 cm²
b   320 cm²
c   160 cm²

5

1

a 8, 80, 800
b 12, 120, 1,200
c 16, 160, 1,600
d 20, 200, 2,000
e 24, 240, 2,400
f 28, 280, 2,800
g 32, 320, 3,200
h 36, 360, 3,600
i 40, 400, 4,000
j 44, 440, 4,400
k 48, 480, 4,800

2

a 112
b 300
c 156
d 228
e 192
f 1,136
g 1,888
h 1,580

6

1 235
2 98
3 231
4 165
5 241
6 168
7 236
8 136
9 146
10 297
11 256
12 79
13 648
14 593
15 345
16 856
17 699

7

1 $28 \div 4 = 7$
2 $12 \times 4 = 48$
3 $8 \times 4 = 32$
4 $44 \div 4 = 11$
5 $9 \times 4 = 36$
6 $£4 \times 4 = £16$
7 $10 \times 4 = 40$
8 $20 \div 4 = 5$
9 $36 \div 4 = 9$
10 $240 \div 4 = 60$
11 $80 \times 4 = 320$
12 $80 \div 4 = 20$
13 $200 \times £4 = £800$
14 $30 \times 4 = 120$

8

1 $\dfrac{2}{5} = \dfrac{8}{\mathbf{20}}$

2 $\dfrac{28}{32} = \dfrac{\mathbf{7}}{8}$

3 $\dfrac{2}{7} = \dfrac{8}{\mathbf{28}}$

4 $\dfrac{44}{48} = \dfrac{\mathbf{11}}{12}$

5 $\dfrac{12}{16} = \dfrac{3}{\mathbf{4}}$

6 $\dfrac{\mathbf{24}}{28} = \dfrac{6}{7}$

7 $\dfrac{12}{44} = \dfrac{\mathbf{3}}{11}$

8 $\dfrac{5}{11} = \dfrac{20}{\mathbf{44}}$

9 $\dfrac{6}{12} = \dfrac{24}{\mathbf{48}}$

10 $\dfrac{4}{\mathbf{40}} = \dfrac{1}{10}$

11 $\dfrac{20}{44} = \dfrac{\mathbf{5}}{11}$

12 $\dfrac{1}{\mathbf{9}} = \dfrac{4}{36}$

13 $\dfrac{2}{11} = \dfrac{\mathbf{8}}{44}$

14 $\dfrac{28}{32} = \dfrac{7}{\mathbf{8}}$

15 $\dfrac{4}{\mathbf{28}} = \dfrac{1}{7}$

16 $\dfrac{\mathbf{6}}{9} = \dfrac{24}{36}$

17 $\dfrac{11}{12} = \dfrac{\mathbf{44}}{48}$

18 $\dfrac{5}{7} = \dfrac{\mathbf{20}}{28}$

19 $\dfrac{8}{11} = \dfrac{\mathbf{32}}{44}$

20 $\dfrac{\mathbf{24}}{32} = \dfrac{6}{8}$

21 $\dfrac{\mathbf{40}}{44} = \dfrac{10}{11}$

22 $\dfrac{4}{12} = \dfrac{16}{\mathbf{48}}$

9

1 32
2 20
3 16
4 12
5 8
6 44
7 40
8 24
9 48
10 36
11 52
12 80
13 200
14 100
15 120
16 60
17 88
18 160

10

1 5
2 8
3 4
4 12
5 3
6 1
7 7
8 9
9 2
10 6
11 11
12 20
13 30
14 70
15 100
16 80
17 110
18 250

11

1 800 ml milk, 12 bananas, 8 chocolate bars
2 800 g oats, 480 g butter, 440 g brown sugar
3 110 g sugar, 100 ml cream, 12 g butter
4 60 g flour, 15 g sugar, 30 g butter, 40 g dried fruit
5 44 strawberries, 36 cherries, 200 ml yoghurt, 400 ml juice

12

1 $10 \text{ cm} \times 4 = 40 \text{ cm}$
2 $12 \text{ cm} \times 4 = 48 \text{ cm}$
3 $4 \text{ cm} \times 4 = 16 \text{ cm}$
4 $11 \text{ cm} \times 4 = 44 \text{ cm}$
5 $8 \text{ cm} \times 4 = 32 \text{ cm}$
6 $9 \text{ cm} \times 4 = 36 \text{ cm}$
7 $4 \text{ cm} \times 5 = 20 \text{ cm}$
8 $4 \text{ cm} \times 6 = 24 \text{ cm}$
9 $4 \text{ cm} \times 8 = 32 \text{ cm}$
10 $4 \text{ cm} \times 10 = 40 \text{ cm}$
11 $40 \text{ cm} \times 5 = 200 \text{ cm}$
12 $40 \text{ cm} \times 8 = 320 \text{ cm}$

5 times table

1

1

1	2	3	4	5	6	7	8	9	10
11	12	13	14	15	16	17	18	19	20
21	22	23	24	25	26	27	28	29	30
31	32	33	34	35	36	37	38	39	40
41	42	43	44	45	46	47	48	49	50
51	52	53	54	55	56	57	58	59	60
61	62	63	64	65	66	67	68	69	70
71	72	73	74	75	76	77	78	79	80
81	82	83	84	85	86	87	88	89	90
91	92	93	94	95	96	97	98	99	100

2

1	x	5	=	5	3	x	5	=	2	11	7	3
2	8	x	5	=	40	12	4	6	x	5	=	30
10	x	5	=	5	8	5	=	45	5	x	4	x
8	x	5	6	3	x	x	30	5	=	5	x	5
x	4	5	=	x	3	5	5	1	10	=	5	=
5	5	x	=	4	x	5	=	20	2	30	8	15
3	9	3	=	50	5	4	x	25	=	20	4	12
6	x	5	=	25	=	11	7	x	5	=	30	x
x	5	5	6	3	10	7	x	5	=	35	3	5
6	=	5	=	30	8	x	5	5	11	x	5	=
5	45	6	x	15	5	=	11	x	5	=	55	60

2

Set 1	Set 2	Set 3	Set 4	Set 5	Set 6	Set 7	Set 8	Set 9
1 x 5 = 5	25 = 5 x 5	7 x 5 = 35	9 = 45 ÷ 5	4 x 5 = 20	7 = 35 ÷ 5	3 x 5 = 15	40 = 8 x 5	8 = 40 ÷ 5
2 x 5 = 10	40 ÷ 5 = 8	8 x 5 = 40	50 ÷ 5 = 10	5 x 5 = 25	8 = 40 ÷ 5	50 = 10 x 5	12 x 5 = 60	9 = 45 ÷ 5
5 ÷ 5 = 1	45 = 9 x 5	50 = 10 x 5	55 ÷ 5 = 11	15 ÷ 5 = 3	9 = 45 ÷ 5	55 = 11 x 5	5 = 1 x 5	45 = 9 x 5
10 ÷ 5 = 2	3 = 15 ÷ 5	55 = 11 x 5	20 = 4 x 5	20 ÷ 5 = 4	50 ÷ 5 = 10	6 = 30 ÷ 5	20 ÷ 5 = 4	50 ÷ 5 = 10
60 ÷ 5 = 12	4 = 20 ÷ 5	11 x 5 = 55	11 = 55 ÷ 5	25 ÷ 5 = 5	55 ÷ 5 = 11	40 = 8 x 5	25 ÷ 5 = 5	55 ÷ 5 = 11
30 = 6 x 5	5 = 25 ÷ 5	6 = 30 ÷ 5	12 = 60 ÷ 5	1 = 5 ÷ 5	30 = 6 x 5	12 x 5 = 60	1 = 5 ÷ 5	20 = 4 x 5
35 = 7 x 5	9 x 5 = 45	10 = 2 x 5	3 x 5 = 15	2 = 10 ÷ 5	35 = 7 x 5	5 = 1 x 5	2 = 10 ÷ 5	11 = 55 ÷ 5
40 = 8 x 5	10 x 5 = 50	15 = 3 x 5	4 x 5 = 20	30 ÷ 5 = 6	40 = 8 x 5	25 = 5 x 5	30 ÷ 5 = 6	12 = 60 ÷ 5
12 x 5 = 60	45 ÷ 5 = 9	7 = 35 ÷ 5	5 x 5 = 25	35 ÷ 5 = 7	12 x 5 = 60	15 ÷ 5 = 3	15 = 3 x 5	45 ÷ 5 = 9
5 = 1 x 5	6 x 5 = 30	8 = 40 ÷ 5	15 ÷ 5 = 3	10 = 50 ÷ 5	5 = 1 x 5		40 ÷ 5 = 8	6 x 5 = 30

3

1

5	20	43	37	18	37	21	62	43	55	68	28	40
23	25	62	26	31	43	72	28	11	32	40	42	14
45	30	45	15	20	5	15	17	21	58	30	45	23
16	11	21	40	17	11	32	15	27	21	36	54	50
27	22	53	60	26	54	38	84	14	20	31	40	35
38	42	27	55	10	20	40	31	12	15	16	30	25
32	26	38	2	25	28	55	45	30	35	15	67	32
43	42	42	5	30	37	19	26	43	25	47	62	54
46	57	49	2	45	42	2	32	31	15	20	40	50
74	54	1	3	12	32	32	45	11	26	15	16	60
56	23	5	6	23	18	54	70	10	18	9	10	exit

2

a	5 + 5 + 5 + 5 + 5 + 5 + 5	7 x 5	35
b	5 + 5 + 5 + 5	4 x 5	20
c	5 + 5 + 5 + 5 + 5 + 5	6 x 5	30
d	5 + 5 + 5 + 5 + 5 + 5 + 5 + 5 + 5 + 5 + 5	11 x 5	55
e	5 + 5	2 x 5	10
f	5 + 5 + 5 + 5 + 5 + 5 + 5 + 5	8 x 5	40
g	5 + 5 + 5 + 5 + 5 + 5 + 5 + 5 + 5 + 5 + 5 + 5	12 x 5	60
h	5	1 x 5	5
i	5 + 5 + 5 + 5 + 5 + 5 + 5 + 5 + 5 + 5	10 x 5	50
j	5 + 5 + 5 + 5 + 5	5 x 5	25
k	5 + 5 + 5 + 5 + 5 + 5 + 5 + 5 + 5	9 x 5	45
l	5 + 5 + 5	3 x 5	15

4

1

a 60 cm²
b 25 cm²
c 45 cm²
d 5 cm²
e 15 cm²
f 50 cm²
g 40 cm²
h 35 cm²
i 30 cm²
j 20 cm²
k 55 cm²

2

a 250 cm²
b 600 cm²
c 200 cm²

ANSWERS

5

1
a 10, 100, 1,000
b 15, 150, 1,500
c 20, 200, 2,000
d 25, 250, 2,500
e 30, 300, 3,000
f 35, 350, 3,500
g 40, 400, 4,000
h 45, 450, 4,500
i 50, 500, 5,000
j 55, 550, 5,500
k 60, 600, 6,000

2
a 140
b 375
c 195
d 285
e 240
f 1,420
g 2,360
h 1,975

6
1 65
2 113
3 93
4 31
5 65
6 173
7 147
8 43
9 107
10 135
11 91
12 73
13 1,107
14 693
15 329
16 1,127
17 1,353

7
1 8 x 5 = 40
2 15 ÷ 5 = 3
3 10 x £5 = £50
4 5 ÷ 5 = 1
5 9 x 5 = 45
6 12 x 5 = 60
7 6 x 5 = 30
8 20 ÷ 5 = 4
9 5 x 5 = 25
10 £500 ÷ 5 = £100
11 £70 x 5 = £350
12 550 ÷ 5 = 110
13 120 x 5 = 600
14 400 ÷ 5 = 80

8
1 $\dfrac{2}{5} = \dfrac{10}{25}$

2 $\dfrac{35}{40} = \dfrac{7}{8}$

3 $\dfrac{2}{7} = \dfrac{10}{35}$

4 $\dfrac{55}{60} = \dfrac{11}{12}$

5 $\dfrac{10}{15} = \dfrac{2}{3}$

6 $\dfrac{30}{35} = \dfrac{6}{7}$

7 $\dfrac{15}{55} = \dfrac{3}{11}$

8 $\dfrac{4}{9} = \dfrac{20}{45}$

9 $\dfrac{3}{11} = \dfrac{15}{55}$

10 $\dfrac{5}{40} = \dfrac{1}{8}$

11 $\dfrac{20}{55} = \dfrac{4}{11}$

12 $\dfrac{1}{6} = \dfrac{5}{30}$

13 $\dfrac{2}{11} = \dfrac{10}{55}$

14 $\dfrac{35}{40} = \dfrac{7}{8}$

15 $\dfrac{5}{25} = \dfrac{1}{5}$

16 $\dfrac{6}{11} = \dfrac{30}{55}$

17 $\dfrac{11}{12} = \dfrac{55}{60}$

18 $\dfrac{4}{7} = \dfrac{20}{35}$

19 $\dfrac{8}{11} = \dfrac{40}{55}$

20 $\dfrac{25}{30} = \dfrac{5}{6}$

21 $\dfrac{50}{55} = \dfrac{10}{11}$

22 $\dfrac{5}{9} = \dfrac{25}{45}$

9
1 40
2 25
3 20
4 15
5 10
6 55
7 50
8 30
9 60
10 45
11 65
12 100
13 250
14 125
15 450
16 110
17 500
18 1,000

10
1 1
2 7
3 5
4 2
5 11
6 10
7 6
8 4
9 8
10 3
11 12
12 20
13 60
14 90
15 40
16 70
17 120
18 100

11
1 1,000 ml milk, 15 bananas, 10 chocolate bars
2 1,000 g oats, 600 g butter, 550 g brown sugar
3 90 g sugar, 80 ml cream, 10 g butter
4 45 g flour, 15 g sugar, 25 g butter, 30 g dried fruit
5 55 strawberries, 45 cherries, 250 ml yoghurt, 500 ml juice

12
1 10 cm x 5 = 50 cm
2 12 cm x 5 = 60 cm
3 4 cm x 5 = 20 cm
4 11 cm x 5 = 55 cm
5 8 cm x 5 = 40 cm
6 9 cm x 5 = 45 cm
7 5 cm x 6 = 30 cm
8 5 cm x 7 = 35 cm
9 5 cm x 12 = 60 cm
10 50 cm x 8 = 400 cm
11 50 cm x 6 = 300 cm
12 50 cm x 7 = 350 cm

6 times table

1

1

1	2	3	4	5	6	7	8	9	10
11	12	13	14	15	16	17	18	19	20
21	22	23	24	25	26	27	28	29	30
31	32	33	34	35	36	37	38	39	40
41	42	43	44	45	46	47	48	49	50
51	52	53	54	55	56	57	58	59	60
61	62	63	64	65	66	67	68	69	70
71	72	73	74	75	76	77	78	79	80
81	82	83	84	85	86	87	88	89	90
91	92	93	94	95	96	97	98	99	100

2

1	x	6	=	6	3	x	6	=	8	x	12	9
2	3	x	6	=	x	8	x	6	x	11	x	x
x	6	11	12	5	x	6	=	30	6	5	6	7
6	5	x	x	8	x	6	=	60	=	x	=	x
=	9	x	6	6	9	6	x	36	48	6	72	6
12	9	x	6	=	=	X	4	x	6	=	20	=
5	x	6	6	=	16	66	6	x	6	25	11	42
5	8	x	6	=	40	10	x	6	=	60	x	66
3	x	6	=	18	54	9	x	6	=	40	6	72
8	x	12	x	6	=	60	11	x	6	48	=	x
7	x	6	=	36	x	4	x	6	=	24	60	6

2

Set 1	Set 2	Set 3	Set 4	Set 5	Set 6	Set 7	Set 8	Set 9
7 x 6 = **42**	6 = **36** ÷ 6	3 x 6 = **18**	**18** ÷ 6 = 3	7 = **42** ÷ 6	**1** = 6 ÷ 6	**18** ÷ 6 = 3	24 = **4** x 6	4 = **24** ÷ 6
60 ÷ 6 = 10	**18** = 3 x 6	42 ÷ 6 = **7**	24 ÷ 6 = **4**	**66** ÷ 6 = 11	2 = **12** ÷ 6	24 ÷ 6 = **4**	18 ÷ 6 = **3**	**11** x 6 = 66
72 ÷ 6 = 12	24 = **4** x 6	**48** ÷ 6 = 8	30 ÷ 6 = **5**	8 = **48** ÷ 6	48 = **8** x 6	**66** = 11 x 6	**24** ÷ 6 = 4	**12** x 6 = 72
1 = **6** ÷ 6	**30** = 5 x 6	54 ÷ 6 = **9**	3 = **18** ÷ 6	**9** = 54 ÷ 6	**54** = 9 x 6	12 x 6 = **72**	66 = **11** x 6	4 x 6 = **24**
2 = **12** ÷ 6	6 ÷ 6 = **1**	**11** x 6 = 66	**4** = 24 ÷ 6	6 = **1** x 6	72 = **12** x 6	**60** = 10 x 6	12 ÷ 6 = **2**	**5** x 6 = 30
48 = 8 x 6	**7** = 42 ÷ 6	12 x 6 = **72**	8 x 6 = 48	**6** x 6 = 36	**11** x 6 = 66	**5** = 30 ÷ 6	**60** = 10 x 6	**36** = 6 x 6
54 = **9** x 6	66 ÷ 6 = **11**	**4** x 6 = 24	**12** = 2 x 6	11 = **66** ÷ 6	**12** x 6 = 72	6 = **36** ÷ 6	**5** = 30 ÷ 6	10 = **60** ÷ 6
72 = 12 x 6	**8** = 48 ÷ 6	5 x 6 = **30**	36 ÷ 6 = **6**	12 = **72** ÷ 6	4 x 6 = **24**	18 = **3** x 6	6 = **36** ÷ 6	**1** x 6 = 6
60 = **10** x 6	9 = **54** ÷ 6	**36** = 6 x 6	9 x 6 = **54**	**3** x 6 = 18	5 x 6 = **30**	**24** = 4 x 6	**18** = 3 x 6	**2** x 6 = 12
5 = **30** ÷ 6	1 x 6 = **6**	42 = **7** x 6	10 x 6 = **60**	**42** ÷ 6 = 7	**36** = 6 x 6	30 = **5** x 6	30 = **5** x 6	8 x 6 = **48**

3

1

6	11	41	33	69	53	26	85	35	47	23	1	60
12	17	19	23	28	72	37	6	24	66	19	18	3
36	18	54	48	36	60	66	8	43	16	3	4	5
31	5	42	4	75	34	60	15	26	13	5	3	24
67	24	60	42	43	18	12	2	24	14	28	34	21
35	4	46	35	57	60	18	8	3	30	42	75	62
27	36	42	22	43	16	6	42	12	18	74	19	25
48	74	57	53	24	46	72	16	61	26	63	11	31
73	25	35	22	89	26	42	18	54	36	30	6	18
35	6	86	11	24	36	67	24	12	3	66	3	72
2	72	37	57	75	22	4	25	64	78	33	6	exit

2

a	6 + 6 + 6	3 x 6	18
b	6 + 6 + 6 + 6 + 6 + 6 + 6 + 6	**8 x 6**	48
c	6 + 6 + 6 + 6 + 6 + 6 + 6 + 6 + 6	**9 x 6**	**54**
d	**6 + 6 + 6 + 6**	**4 x 6**	24
e	**6 + 6 + 6 + 6 + 6 + 6**	6 x 6	**36**
f	6 + 6 + 6 + 6 + 6 + 6 + 6 + 6 + 6 + 6 + 6 + 6	**12 x 6**	**72**
g	**6**	**1 x 6**	6
h	**6 + 6 + 6 + 6 + 6 + 6 + 6**	7 x 6	**42**
i	6 + 6 + 6 + 6 + 6 + 6 + 6 + 6 + 6 + 6 + 6	**11 x 6**	66
j	**6 + 6 + 6 + 6 + 6 + 6 + 6 + 6 + 6 + 6**	10 x 6	60
k	6 + 6	2 x 6	**12**
l	6 + 6 + 6 + 6 + 6	**5 x 6**	**30**

4

1

a 6 cm²
b 72 cm²
c 36 cm²
d 24 cm²
e 12 cm²
f 48 cm²
g 54 cm²
h 60 cm²
i 30 cm²
j 42 cm²
k 66 cm²

2

a 300 cm²
b 720 cm²
c 240 cm²

ANSWERS

5

1

a 12, 120, 1,200
b 18, 180, 1,800
c 24, 240, 2,400
d 30, 300, 3,000
e 36, 360, 3,600
f 42, 420, 4,200
g 48, 480, 4,800
h 54, 540, 5,400
i 60, 600, 6,000
j 66, 660 6,600
k 72, 720, 7,200

2

a 168
b 450
c 234
d 342
e 288
f 1,704
g 2,832
h 2,370

6

1 123
2 253
3 241
4 88
5 156
6 325
7 254
8 412
9 523
10 369
11 246
12 196
13 351
14 453
15 394
16 475
17 632

7

1 8 x 6 = 48
2 12 x 6 = 72
3 54 ÷ 6 = 9
4 66 ÷ 6 = 11
5 4 x 6 = 24
6 £18 ÷ 6 = £3
7 36 g ÷ 6 = 6 g
8 7 x 6 = 42
9 6 x 6 = 36
10 360 ÷ 6 = 60
11 420 ÷ 6 = 70
12 8 x 60 g = 480 g
13 20 x 6 = 120
14 200 x 6 = 1,200

8

1 $\dfrac{2}{5} = \dfrac{\mathbf{12}}{30}$

2 $\dfrac{42}{\mathbf{48}} = \dfrac{7}{8}$

3 $\dfrac{2}{7} = \dfrac{\mathbf{12}}{42}$

4 $\dfrac{66}{72} = \dfrac{11}{\mathbf{12}}$

5 $\dfrac{\mathbf{12}}{18} = \dfrac{2}{3}$

6 $\dfrac{36}{42} = \dfrac{6}{\mathbf{7}}$

7 $\dfrac{\mathbf{18}}{66} = \dfrac{3}{11}$

8 $\dfrac{4}{8} = \dfrac{\mathbf{24}}{48}$

9 $\dfrac{4}{11} = \dfrac{24}{\mathbf{66}}$

10 $\dfrac{6}{42} = \dfrac{\mathbf{1}}{7}$

11 $\dfrac{\mathbf{24}}{48} = \dfrac{4}{8}$

12 $\dfrac{1}{5} = \dfrac{6}{\mathbf{30}}$

13 $\dfrac{\mathbf{3}}{11} = \dfrac{18}{66}$

14 $\dfrac{42}{48} = \dfrac{7}{8}$

15 $\dfrac{6}{24} = \dfrac{\mathbf{1}}{4}$

16 $\dfrac{5}{11} = \dfrac{30}{\mathbf{66}}$

17 $\dfrac{10}{12} = \dfrac{\mathbf{60}}{72}$

18 $\dfrac{4}{7} = \dfrac{\mathbf{24}}{42}$

19 $\dfrac{8}{11} = \dfrac{\mathbf{48}}{66}$

20 $\dfrac{36}{48} = \dfrac{6}{\mathbf{8}}$

21 $\dfrac{60}{66} = \dfrac{\mathbf{10}}{11}$

22 $\dfrac{4}{10} = \dfrac{24}{\mathbf{60}}$

9

1 48
2 30
3 24
4 18
5 12
6 66
7 60
8 36
9 72
10 54
11 78
12 120
13 300
14 600
15 90
16 180
17 360
18 240

10

1 3
2 9
3 4
4 11
5 5
6 10
7 6
8 8
9 2
10 12
11 1
12 20
13 100
14 40
15 110
16 13
17 30
18 200

11

1 1,200 ml milk, 18 bananas, 12 chocolate bars
2 1,200 g oats, 720 g butter, 660 g brown sugar
3 70 g sugar, 60 ml cream, 8 g butter
4 40 g flour, 12 g sugar, 20 g butter, 30 g dried fruit
5 66 strawberries, 54 cherries, 300 ml yoghurt, 600 ml juice

12

1 10 cm x 6 = 60 cm
2 12 cm x 6 = 72 cm
3 4 cm x 6 = 24 cm
4 11 cm x 6 = 66 cm
5 8 cm x 6 = 48 cm
6 9 cm x 6 = 54 cm
7 6 cm x 8 = 48 cm
8 6 cm x 7 = 42 cm
9 6 cm x 5 = 30 cm
10 6 cm x 10 = 60 cm
11 60 cm x 7 = 420 cm
12 60 cm x 4 = 240 cm

7 times table

1

1

1	2	3	4	5	6	7	8	9	10
11	12	13	14	15	16	17	18	19	20
21	22	23	24	25	26	27	28	29	30
31	32	33	34	35	36	37	38	39	40
41	42	43	44	45	46	47	48	49	50
51	52	53	54	55	56	57	58	59	60
61	62	63	64	65	66	67	68	69	70
71	72	73	74	75	76	77	78	79	80
81	82	83	84	85	86	87	88	89	90
91	92	93	94	95	96	97	98	99	100

2

1	x	7	=	7	70	x	7	42	7	8	56	1
12	77	14	6	x	7	=	42	77	x	x	11	x
9	x	12	x	2	70	3	84	63	7	7	x	7
10	X	7	X	12	x	18	x	14	=	=	7	=
4	x	7	=	7	56	7	28	7	49	63	=	70
x	3	7	63	84	4	35	=	56	=	70	77	12
7	21	7	=	12	x	6	5	14	77	9	84	x
=	84	7	8	70	7	49	x	x	49	x	21	7
21	56	3	x	7	=	21	14	7	7	7	14	=
28	3	x	7	=	28	35	28	42	=	=	70	56
8	x	7	=	56	8	x	7	=	63	63	35	7

2

Set 1	Set 2	Set 3	Set 4	Set 5	Set 6	Set 7	Set 8	Set 9
$1 \times 7 = 7$	$6 \times 7 = 42$	$35 \div 7 = 5$	$4 = 28 \div 7$	$8 \times 7 = 56$	$28 \div 7 = 4$	$14 \div 7 = 2$	$11 = 77 \div 7$	$10 = 70 \div 7$
$4 \times 7 = 28$	$7 \times 7 = 49$	$5 = 35 \div 7$	$7 = 49 \div 7$	$9 \times 7 = 63$	$35 \div 7 = 5$	$21 \div 7 = 3$	$42 \div 7 = 6$	$11 = 77 \div 7$
$11 \times 7 = 77$	$10 \times 7 = 70$	$8 \times 7 = 56$	$8 = 56 \div 7$	$6 = 42 \div 7$	$5 = 35 \div 7$	$70 = 7 \times 10$	$49 \div 7 = 7$	$42 \div 7 = 6$
$12 \times 7 = 84$	$56 = 7 \times 8$	$9 \times 7 = 63$	$9 = 63 \div 7$	$35 = 7 \times 5$	$8 \times 7 = 56$	$77 = 7 \times 11$	$56 \div 7 = 8$	$49 \div 7 = 7$
$7 = 7 \times 1$	$63 = 7 \times 9$	$6 = 42 \div 7$	$84 \div 7 = 12$	$10 = 70 \div 7$	$9 \times 7 = 63$	$7 \times 7 = 49$	$21 = 7 \times 3$	$56 \div 7 = 8$
$49 = 7 \times 7$	$70 = 7 \times 10$	$35 = 7 \times 5$	$1 = 7 \div 7$	$11 = 77 \div 7$	$6 = 42 \div 7$	$10 \times 7 = 70$	$28 = 7 \times 4$	$3 = 21 \div 7$
$5 \times 7 = 35$	$77 = 7 \times 11$	$10 = 70 \div 7$	$12 = 84 \div 7$	$42 = 7 \times 6$	$35 = 7 \times 5$	$56 = 7 \times 8$	$6 \times 7 = 42$	$4 = 28 \div 7$
$2 = 14 \div 7$	$84 = 7 \times 12$	$11 = 77 \div 7$	$77 \div 7 = 11$	$49 \div 7 = 7$	$10 = 70 \div 7$	$63 = 7 \times 9$	$7 \times 7 = 49$	$42 = 7 \times 6$
$21 = 7 \times 3$	$7 \div 7 = 1$	$42 \div 7 = 6$	$2 \times 7 = 14$	$56 \div 7 = 8$	$11 = 77 \div 7$	$84 = 7 \times 12$	$3 = 21 \div 7$	$28 \div 7 = 4$
$28 = 7 \times 4$	$14 \div 7 = 2$	$49 \div 7 = 7$	$3 \times 7 = 21$	$3 = 21 \div 7$	$42 \div 7 = 6$	$7 \div 7 = 1$	$4 = 28 \div 7$	$84 = 7 \times 12$

3

1

14	35	67	42	68	22	99	65	45	74	24	34	77
7	22	35	49	63	44	85	24	78	23	24	33	57
14	22	44	7	32	45	4	78	1	6	8	35	70
28	35	42	84	49	27	7	25	77	24	64	25	86
56	64	24	64	56	77	70	90	75	23	66	24	76
63	24	12	65	63	34	22	35	86	35	77	32	35
19	64	49	42	14	64	45	28	24	32	56	87	46
33	24	88	86	7	28	70	77	63	56	27	32	24
79	68	54	35	77	35	76	23	75	14	21	56	65
97	34	23	89	33	77	99	32	24	79	28	3	25
42	24	68	24	26	64	35	32	56	88	49	21	exit

2

a	$7 + 7 + 7 + 7$	4×7	28
b	$7 + 7 + 7 + 7 + 7 + 7 + 7 + 7 + 7 + 7 + 7$	11×7	77
c	$7 + 7 + 7 + 7 + 7$	5×7	35
d	$7 + 7 + 7 + 7 + 7 + 7 + 7 + 7 + 7 + 7$	10×7	70
e	7	1×7	7
f	$7 + 7 + 7 + 7 + 7 + 7$	6×7	42
g	$7 + 7 + 7 + 7 + 7 + 7 + 7 + 7 + 7 + 7 + 7 + 7$	12×7	84
h	$7 + 7 + 7 + 7 + 7 + 7 + 7 + 7 + 7$	9×7	63
i	$7 + 7 + 7$	3×7	21
j	$7 + 7 + 7 + 7 + 7 + 7 + 7$	7×7	49
k	$7 + 7 + 7 + 7 + 7 + 7 + 7 + 7$	8×7	56
l	$7 + 7$	2×7	14

4

1

a 7 cm^2
b 49 cm^2
c 42 cm^2
d 56 cm^2
e 77 cm^2
f 21 cm^2
g 35 cm^2
h 84 cm^2
i 63 cm^2
j 70 cm^2
k 14 cm^2

2

a 350 cm^2
b 840 cm^2
c 280 cm^2

ANSWERS

5

1

a 14, 140, 1,400
b 21, 210, 2,100
c 28, 280, 2,800
d 35, 350, 3,500
e 42, 420, 4,200
f 49, 490, 4,900
g 56, 560, 5,600
h 63, 630, 6,300
i 70, 700, 7,000
j 77, 770, 7,700
k 84, 840, 8,400

2

a 196
b 525
c 273
d 399
e 336
f 1,988
g 3,304
h 2,765

6

1 256
2 163
3 196
4 265
5 325
6 142
7 145
8 298
9 658
10 356
11 352
12 289
13 254
14 544
15 653
16 534
17 358

7

1 12 x 7 = 84
2 84 ÷ 7 = 12
3 7 x 7 = 49
4 8 x 7 = 56
5 7 ÷ 7 = 1
6 42 ÷ 7 = 6
7 28 ÷ 7 = 4
8 9 x 7 = 63
9 35 ÷ 7 = 5
10 40 x 7 = 280
11 20 x 7 = 140
12 350 ÷ 7 = 50
13 80 x 7 = 560
14 400 x 7 = 2,800

8

1 $\dfrac{2}{3} = \dfrac{14}{\mathbf{21}}$

2 $\dfrac{49}{56} = \dfrac{\mathbf{7}}{8}$

3 $\dfrac{3}{5} = \dfrac{\mathbf{21}}{35}$

4 $\dfrac{77}{84} = \dfrac{11}{\mathbf{12}}$

5 $\dfrac{10}{11} = \dfrac{\mathbf{70}}{77}$

6 $\dfrac{28}{35} = \dfrac{4}{\mathbf{5}}$

7 $\dfrac{14}{56} = \dfrac{2}{\mathbf{8}}$

8 $\dfrac{4}{12} = \dfrac{\mathbf{28}}{84}$

9 $\dfrac{3}{11} = \dfrac{21}{\mathbf{77}}$

10 $\dfrac{7}{\mathbf{42}} = \dfrac{1}{6}$

11 $\dfrac{\mathbf{7}}{28} = \dfrac{1}{4}$

12 $\dfrac{1}{7} = \dfrac{7}{\mathbf{49}}$

13 $\dfrac{5}{11} = \dfrac{\mathbf{35}}{77}$

14 $\dfrac{\mathbf{35}}{56} = \dfrac{5}{8}$

15 $\dfrac{7}{35} = \dfrac{\mathbf{1}}{5}$

16 $\dfrac{3}{11} = \dfrac{21}{\mathbf{77}}$

17 $\dfrac{11}{12} = \dfrac{\mathbf{77}}{84}$

18 $\dfrac{4}{7} = \dfrac{28}{\mathbf{49}}$

19 $\dfrac{8}{11} = \dfrac{56}{\mathbf{77}}$

20 $\dfrac{\mathbf{35}}{42} = \dfrac{5}{6}$

21 $\dfrac{\mathbf{70}}{77} = \dfrac{10}{11}$

22 $\dfrac{5}{9} = \dfrac{35}{\mathbf{63}}$

9

1 49
2 28
3 21
4 77
5 70
6 84
7 63
8 42
9 14
10 35
11 175
12 140
13 350
14 105
15 210
16 420
17 280
18 630

10

1 8
2 2
3 6
4 10
5 4
6 11
7 5
8 12
9 1
10 7
11 9
12 110
13 20
14 100
15 13
16 30
17 70
18 50

11

1 1,400 ml milk, 21 bananas, 14 chocolate bars
2 1,400 g oats, 840 g butter, 770 g brown sugar
3 60 g sugar, 70 ml cream, 50 g butter
4 30 g flour, 11 g sugar, 20 g butter, 10 g dried fruit
5 77 strawberries, 63 cherries, 350 ml yoghurt, 700 ml juice

12

1 10 cm x 7 = 70 cm
2 12 cm x 7 = 84 cm
3 4 cm x 7 = 28 cm
4 11 cm x 7 = 77 cm
5 8 cm x 7 = 56 cm
6 9 cm x 7 = 63 cm
7 7 cm x 10 = 70 cm
8 7 cm x 6 = 42 cm
9 7 cm x 7 = 49 cm
10 70 cm x 4 = 280 cm
11 70 cm x 3 = 210 cm
12 70 cm x 9 = 630 cm

8 times table

1

1

1	2	3	4	5	6	7	8	9	10
11	12	13	14	15	16	17	18	19	20
21	22	23	24	25	26	27	28	29	30
31	32	33	34	35	36	37	38	39	40
41	42	43	44	45	46	47	48	49	50
51	52	53	54	55	56	57	58	59	60
61	62	63	64	65	66	67	68	69	70
71	72	73	74	75	76	77	78	79	80
81	82	83	84	85	86	87	88	89	90
91	92	93	94	95	96	97	98	99	100

2

1	x	8	=	8	x	4	x	8	=	12	32	4
48	12	x	8	=	88	5	x	8	=	x	8	x
11	3	8	=	8	7	48	56	72	64	8	80	8
96	x	8	x	5	x	8	=	40	16	=	6	=
8	8	8	16	8	8	x	16	9	32	96	x	32
56	=	64	=	24	=	40	40	x	9	6	8	6
2	32	72	8	88	56	64	88	8	x	x	=	x
3	x	8	=	24	80	64	88	=	8	8	48	8
8	x	8	5	x	8	=	48	80	=	=	32	=
16	24	x	=	4	x	8	=	44	72	96	=	88
3	x	8	=	16	10	x	8	=	80	8	8	24

2

Set 1	Set 2	Set 3	Set 4	Set 5	Set 6	Set 7	Set 8	Set 9
1 x 8 = **8**	**56** = 7 x 8	**3** = 24 ÷ 8	12 = **96** ÷ 8	**8** = 1 x 8	5 = **40** ÷ 8	24 ÷ 8 = **3**	**16** = 2 x 8	**12** = 96 ÷ 8
2 x 8 = 16	16 ÷ 8 = **2**	**64** = 8 x 8	**9** x 8 = 72	**16** = 2 x 8	**88** = 11 x 8	**8** x 8 = 64	**3** x 8 = 24	**9** x 8 = 72
80 ÷ 8 = 10	24 ÷ 8 = **3**	**72** = 9 x 8	**10** x 8 = 80	**3** x 8 = 24	96 = **12** x 8	**24** = 3 x 8	24 ÷ 8 = 3	10 x 8 = **80**
88 ÷ 8 = **11**	**8** x 8 = 64	80 = **10** x 8	11 x 8 = **88**	**40** = 5 x 8	8 ÷ 8 = **1**	32 = **4** x 8	8 x 8 = **64**	**16** = 8 ÷ 2
96 ÷ 8 = 12	**24** = 3 x 8	72 ÷ 8 = **9**	4 x 8 = **32**	8 = **64** ÷ 8	**12** = 96 ÷ 8	**32** ÷ 8 = 4	**24** = 3 x 8	**24** ÷ 8 = 3
1 = **8** ÷ 8	32 = **4** x 8	4 = **32** ÷ 8	**5** x 8 = 40	**6** x 8 = 48	9 x 8 = 72	**56** ÷ 8 = 7	32 ÷ 8 = 4	8 x 8 = **64**
9 = **72** ÷ 8	32 ÷ 8 = **4**	5 = **40** ÷ 8	**7** x 8 = 56	**6** = 48 ÷ 8	10 x 8 = **80**	64 ÷ 8 = **8**	**32** ÷ 8 = 4	**24** = 3 x 8
10 = 80 ÷ 8	56 ÷ 8 = **7**	**88** = 11 x 8	12 x 8 = **96**	7 = **56** ÷ 8	**11** x 8 = 88	**2** = 16 ÷ **8**	40 = **5** x 8	32 = **4** x 8
11 = **88** ÷ 8	**64** ÷ 8 = 8	96 = **12** x 8	8 = **1** x 8	40 ÷ 8 = **5**	4 x 8 = **32**	**3** = 24 ÷ 8	8 = **64** ÷ 8	11 x 8 = **88**
48 = **6** x 8	2 = **16** ÷ 8	8 ÷ 8 = **1**	16 = **2** x 8	**48** ÷ 8 = 6	5 x 8 = **40**	64 = **8** x 8	**6** x 8 = 48	4 x 8 = **32**

3

1

8	48	16	40	96	88	64	56	37	52	47	24	28
53	24	40	53	65	57	72	45	79	48	42	23	64
35	23	48	67	36	16	80	11	22	56	36	36	35
31	57	43	89	32	38	88	16	24	32	53	45	23
35	16	76	99	34	35	72	34	36	56	64	13	53
75	71	35	8	12	44	10	23	35	54	72	80	56
35	6	56	4	8	32	43	68	57	21	80	55	42
90	3	53	48	19	78	50	65	64	37	8	35	53
43	6	7	24	64	48	40	64	16	32	16	26	32
78	40	24	46	79	43	46	70	72	26	25	32	25
88	22	62	32	34	35	43	45	96	80	88	16	exit

2

a	8 + 8 + 8 + 8	4 x 8	32
b	8	1 x 8	**8**
c	**8 + 8 + 8 + 8 + 8 + 8 + 8 + 8 + 8 + 8**	**10 x 8**	80
d	8 + 8 + 8 + 8 + 8 + 8 + 8 + 8 + 8 + 8 + 8 + 8	**12 x 8**	**96**
e	8 + 8 + 8 + 8 + 8	**5 x 8**	40
f	**8 + 8 + 8 + 8 + 8 + 8 + 8 + 8 + 8 + 8 + 8**	11 x 8	**88**
g	**8 + 8 + 8 + 8 + 8 + 8 + 8**	**7 x 8**	56
h	8 + 8 + 8 + 8 + 8 + 8 + 8 + 8	**8 x 8**	**64**
i	8 + 8 + 8	**3 x 8**	24
j	**8 + 8 + 8 + 8 + 8 + 8 + 8 + 8 + 8**	**9 x 8**	72
k	8 + 8	2 x 8	**16**
l	8 + 8 + 8 + 8 + 8 + 8	**6 x 8**	48

4

1

a 8 cm²
b 72 cm²
c 80 cm²
d 88 cm²
e 48 cm²
f 24 cm²
g 64 cm²
h 16 cm²
i 96 cm²
j 32 cm²
k 40 cm²

2

a 400 cm²
b 960 cm²
c 320 cm²

ANSWERS

5

1

a 16, 160, 1,600
b 24, 240, 2,400
c 32, 320, 3,200
d 40, 400, 4,000
e 48, 480, 4,800
f 56, 560, 5,600
g 64, 640, 6,400
h 72, 720, 7,200
i 80, 800, 8,000
j 88, 880, 8,800
k 96, 960, 9,600

2

a 224
b 600
c 312
d 456
e 384
f 2,272
g 3,776
h 3,160

6

1 41
2 235
3 98
4 76
5 75
6 153
7 145
8 325
9 251
10 85
11 167
12 253
13 154
14 236
15 174
16 226
17 846

7

1 12 x 8 = 96
2 48 ÷ 8 = 6
3 56 ÷ 8 = 7
4 2 x 8 = 16
5 £72 ÷ 8 = £9
6 11 x 8 = 88
7 5 x 8 = 40
8 96 ÷ 8 = 12
9 8 ÷ 8 = 1
10 480 ÷ 8 = 60
11 240 ÷ 8 = 30
12 200 x 8 = 1,600
13 30 x 8 = 240
14 20 x 8 = 160

8

1 $\frac{3}{5} = \frac{24}{\mathbf{40}}$

2 $\frac{1}{4} = \frac{\mathbf{8}}{32}$

3 $\frac{72}{96} = \frac{9}{\mathbf{12}}$

4 $\frac{40}{\mathbf{80}} = \frac{5}{10}$

5 $\frac{\mathbf{7}}{8} = \frac{56}{\mathbf{64}}$

6 $\frac{80}{88} = \frac{\mathbf{10}}{11}$

7 $\frac{5}{6} = \frac{\mathbf{40}}{48}$

8 $\frac{\mathbf{24}}{40} = \frac{3}{5}$

9 $\frac{4}{\mathbf{11}} = \frac{32}{88}$

10 $\frac{8}{72} = \frac{\mathbf{1}}{9}$

11 $\frac{32}{72} = \frac{4}{\mathbf{9}}$

12 $\frac{2}{6} = \frac{\mathbf{16}}{48}$

13 $\frac{9}{\mathbf{11}} = \frac{72}{88}$

14 $\frac{7}{10} = \frac{\mathbf{56}}{80}$

15 $\frac{\mathbf{40}}{88} = \frac{5}{11}$

16 $\frac{6}{11} = \frac{48}{\mathbf{88}}$

17 $\frac{\mathbf{11}}{12} = \frac{88}{96}$

18 $\frac{4}{7} = \frac{32}{\mathbf{56}}$

19 $\frac{8}{11} = \frac{\mathbf{64}}{88}$

20 $\frac{40}{48} = \frac{\mathbf{5}}{6}$

21 $\frac{80}{96} = \frac{10}{\mathbf{12}}$

22 $\frac{5}{9} = \frac{40}{\mathbf{72}}$

9

1 32
2 64
3 24
4 88
5 80
6 96
7 72
8 48
9 16
10 40
11 200
12 160
13 400
14 120
15 240
16 480
17 800
18 880

10

1 8
2 1
3 4
4 6
5 9
6 2
7 7
8 11
9 10
10 5
11 12
12 60
13 100
14 40
15 50
16 110
17 20
18 1,000

11

1 1,600 ml milk, 24 bananas, 16 chocolate bars
2 1,600 g oats, 960 g butter, 880 g brown sugar
3 60 g sugar, 50 ml cream, 7 g butter
4 30 g flour, 9 g sugar, 20 g butter, 12 g dried fruit
5 88 strawberries, 72 cherries, 400 ml yoghurt, 800 ml juice

12

1 10 cm x 8 = 80 cm
2 12 cm x 8 = 96 cm
3 4 cm x 8 = 32 cm
4 11 cm x 8 = 88 cm
5 8 cm x 8 = 64 cm
6 9 cm x 8 = 72 cm
7 8 cm x 5 = 40 cm
8 8 cm x 6 = 48 cm
9 8 cm x 3 = 24 cm
10 80 cm x 4 = 320 cm
11 80 cm x 9 = 720 cm
12 80 cm x 10 = 800 cm

9 times table

1

1

1	2	3	4	5	6	7	8	**9**	10
11	12	13	14	15	16	17	**18**	19	20
21	22	23	24	25	26	**27**	28	29	30
31	32	33	34	35	**36**	37	38	39	40
41	42	43	44	**45**	46	47	48	49	50
51	52	53	**54**	55	56	57	58	59	60
61	62	**63**	64	65	66	67	68	69	70
71	**72**	73	74	75	76	77	78	79	80
81	82	83	84	85	86	87	88	89	**90**
91	92	93	94	95	96	97	98	**99**	100

2

1	x	9	=	9	4	72	36	12	x	9	=	108
5	10	9	x	4	x	27	2	x	9	=	81	9
11	x	9	=	99	9	7	=	x	81	11	45	8
6	9	7	x	9	=	90	x	4	9	3	99	x
x	=	3	63	6	54	72	x	9	x	=	10	9
9	90	6	4	5	x	9	=	45	=	9	18	=
=	4	1	x	x	90	9	3	90	12	63	90	72
45	81	54	9	54	72	8	=	x	2	x	36	x
3	x	9	=	27	x	18	36	54	9	45	108	63
108	7	9	36	x	27	11	x	9	=	90	9	=
4	x	9	=	81	=	99	9	x	9	=	81	18

2

Set 1	Set 2	Set 3	Set 4	Set 5	Set 6	Set 7	Set 8	Set 9
1 x 9 = **9**	**54** ÷ 9 = 6	90 = **10** x 9	**27** ÷ 9 = 3	**81** ÷ 9 = 9	2 = **18** ÷ 9	**45** = 5 x 9	99 = **11** x 9	**72** ÷ 9 = 8
5 = **45** ÷ 9	7 = **63** ÷ 9	99 = **11** x 9	2 = **18** ÷ 9	90 ÷ 9 = **10**	**108** ÷ 9 = 12	54 = **6** x 9	**108** = 12 x 9	36 = **4** x 9
99 ÷ 9 = 11	8 = **72** ÷ 9	**108** = 12 x 9	**108** ÷ 9 = 12	18 = **2** x 9	1 = **9** ÷ 9	**18** ÷ 9 = 2	36 = **4** x 9	54 ÷ 9 = **6**
3 x 9 = 27	**7** x 9 = 63	**36** ÷ 9 = 4	1 = **9** ÷ 9	**27** = 3 x 9	12 x 9 = **108**	8 = **72** ÷ 9	45 ÷ 9 = **5**	7 = 63 ÷ 9
4 x 9 = **36**	8 x 9 = **72**	45 ÷ 9 = **5**	**12** x 9 = 108	10 = **90** ÷ 9	9 = **1** x 9	7 x 9 = **63**	**9** ÷ 9 = 1	8 = 72 ÷ 9
10 x 9 = 90	**63** = 7 x 9	9 ÷ 9 = **1**	9 = **1** x 9	2 x 9 = **18**	6 = 54 ÷ 9	**8** x 9 = 72	9 x 9 = 81	**108** ÷ 9 = 12
11 x 9 = **99**	72 = **8** x 9	**9** x 9 = 81	6 = **54** ÷ 9	**3** = 27 ÷ 9	9 = **81** ÷ 9	63 = **7** x 9	**9** x 9 = 81	**1** = 9 ÷ 9
63 ÷ 9 = **7**	**5** x 9 = 45	**45** = 5 x 9	**9** = 81 ÷ 9	4 = **36** ÷ 9	81 ÷ 9 = **9**	72 = 8 x 9	**45** = 5 x 9	**12** x 9 = 108
72 ÷ 9 = 8	**6** x 9 = 54	54 = **6** x 9	**81** ÷ 9 = 9	**11** = 99 ÷ 9	**90** ÷ 9 = 10	27 ÷ 9 = **3**	54 = **6** x 9	9 = **1** x 9
36 = **4** x 9	81 = **9** x 9	18 ÷ 9 = **2**	90 ÷ 9 = **10**	12 = **108** ÷ 9	**18** = 2 x 9	2 = **18** ÷ 9	**18** ÷ 9 = 2	6 = **54** ÷ 9
							27 ÷ 9 = 3	

3

1

18	45	78	42	77	99	44	57	87	32	12	77	89
27	32	56	86	22	55	77	6	2	14	5	75	63
54	33	89	32	57	88	14	8	18	63	11	34	88
45	23	68	56	78	96	33	36	27	89	12	18	81
108	24	53	23	6	53	19	7	36	32	65	36	72
63	90	99	45	54	27	63	9	90	99	63	27	18
72	53	19	81	29	89	39	49	59	90	22	11	27
45	67	75	72	52	65	85	107	65	72	19	54	108
63	42	34	90	90	42	36	75	42	90	32	37	99
9	78	86	108	68	68	104	108	53	24	99	65	90
65	25	47	4	53	9	75	36	90	53	24	97	exit

2

a	9 + 9 + 9	3 x 9	27
b	9 + 9 + 9 + 9 + 9 + 9 + 9 + 9	8 x 9	**72**
c	**9 + 9**	2 x 9	18
d	9 + 9 + 9 + 9 + 9 + 9 + 9	**7 x 9**	**63**
e	**9 + 9 + 9 + 9 + 9 + 9 + 9 + 9 + 9 + 9 + 9**	**11 x 9**	99
f	9	**1 x 9**	9
g	**9 + 9 + 9 + 9 + 9 + 9 + 9 + 9 + 9 + 9 + 9 + 9**	**12 x 9**	108
h	9 + 9 + 9 + 9 + 9 + 9 + 9 + 9 + 9 + 9	**10 x 9**	**90**
i	**9 + 9 + 9 + 9 + 9 + 9**	6 x 9	**54**
j	**9 + 9 + 9 + 9 + 9 + 9 + 9 + 9 + 9**	**9 x 9**	81
k	9 + 9 + 9 + 9 + 9	**5 x 9**	**45**
l	9 + 9 + 9 + 9	**4 x 9**	36

4

1

a 63 cm²
b 9 cm²
c 81 cm²
d 72 cm²
e 90 cm²
f 99 cm²
g 45 cm²
h 54 cm²
i 27 cm²
j 36 cm²
k 108 cm²

2

a 450 cm²
b 1,080 cm²
c 360 cm²

ANSWERS

5

1

a 18, 180, 1,800
b 27, 270, 2,700
c 36, 360, 3,600
d 45, 450, 4,500
e 54, 540, 5,400
f 63, 630, 6,300
g 72, 720, 7,200
h 81, 810, 8,100
i 90, 900, 9,000
j 99, 990, 9,900
k 108, 1,080, 10,800

2

a 252
b 675
c 351
d 513
e 432
f 2,556
g 4,248
h 3,555

6

1 123
2 322
3 86
4 76
5 69
6 245
7 165
8 108
9 563
10 523
11 157
12 485
13 742
14 663
15 265
16 268
17 652

7

1 7 x 9 = 63
2 108 g ÷ 9 = 12 g
3 27 ÷ 9 = 3
4 8 x 9 = 72
5 99 ÷ 9 = 11
6 2 x 9 = 18
7 6 x 9 = 54
8 7 x 9 = 63
9 90 ÷ 9 = 10
10 50 x 9 = 450
11 90 x 9 = 810
12 120 x 9 = 1,080
13 30 x 9 = 270
14 180 ÷ 9 = 20

8

1 $\dfrac{2}{3} = \dfrac{18}{\mathbf{27}}$

2 $\dfrac{63}{72} = \dfrac{\mathbf{7}}{8}$

3 $\dfrac{3}{\mathbf{5}} = \dfrac{27}{45}$

4 $\dfrac{\mathbf{99}}{108} = \dfrac{11}{12}$

5 $\dfrac{10}{11} = \dfrac{\mathbf{90}}{99}$

6 $\dfrac{36}{45} = \dfrac{4}{\mathbf{5}}$

7 $\dfrac{18}{72} = \dfrac{\mathbf{2}}{8}$

8 $\dfrac{4}{12} = \dfrac{36}{\mathbf{108}}$

9 $\dfrac{\mathbf{3}}{11} = \dfrac{27}{99}$

10 $\dfrac{9}{54} = \dfrac{\mathbf{1}}{6}$

11 $\dfrac{9}{\mathbf{36}} = \dfrac{1}{4}$

12 $\dfrac{1}{7} = \dfrac{\mathbf{9}}{63}$

13 $\dfrac{\mathbf{5}}{11} = \dfrac{45}{99}$

14 $\dfrac{45}{72} = \dfrac{5}{\mathbf{8}}$

15 $\dfrac{9}{45} = \dfrac{1}{\mathbf{5}}$

16 $\dfrac{3}{11} = \dfrac{\mathbf{27}}{99}$

17 $\dfrac{11}{\mathbf{12}} = \dfrac{99}{108}$

18 $\dfrac{4}{7} = \dfrac{\mathbf{36}}{63}$

19 $\dfrac{8}{11} = \dfrac{72}{\mathbf{99}}$

20 $\dfrac{45}{54} = \dfrac{\mathbf{5}}{6}$

21 $\dfrac{\mathbf{90}}{99} = \dfrac{10}{11}$

22 $\dfrac{5}{9} = \dfrac{45}{\mathbf{81}}$

9

1 63
2 36
3 27
4 99
5 90
6 108
7 81
8 54
9 18
10 45
11 225
12 180
13 450
14 135
15 270
16 540
17 630
18 360

10

1 9
2 1
3 6
4 8
5 4
6 2
7 10
8 5
9 12
10 7
11 11
12 20
13 110
14 50
15 120
16 90
17 16
18 30

11

1 1,800 ml milk, 27 bananas, 18 chocolate bars
2 1,800 g oats, 1,080 g butter, 990 g brown sugar
3 60 g sugar, 50 ml cream, 40 g butter
4 30 g flour, 11 g sugar, 20 g butter, 10 g dried fruit
5 99 strawberries, 81 cherries, 450 ml yoghurt, 900 ml juice

12

1 10 cm x 9 = 90 cm
2 12 cm x 9 = 108 cm
3 4 cm x 9 = 36 cm
4 11 cm x 9 = 99 cm
5 8 cm x 9 = 72 cm
6 9 cm x 9 = 81 cm
7 9 cm x 8 = 72 cm
8 9 cm x 10 = 90 cm
9 9 cm x 5 = 45 cm
10 90 cm x 4 = 360 cm
11 90 cm x 3 = 270 cm
12 90cm x 6 = 540 cm

10 times table

1

1

1	2	3	4	5	6	7	8	9	10
11	12	13	14	15	16	17	18	19	20
21	22	23	24	25	26	27	28	29	30
31	32	33	34	35	36	37	38	39	40
41	42	43	44	45	46	47	48	49	50
51	52	53	54	55	56	57	58	59	60
61	62	63	64	65	66	67	68	69	70
71	72	73	74	75	76	77	78	79	80
81	82	83	84	85	86	87	88	89	90
91	92	93	94	95	96	97	98	99	100

2

1	x	10	=	10	3	80	100	2	4	12	2	6
11	11	1	x	10	=	100	9	x	50	x	x	40
7	x	x	6	2	110	5	x	10	5	10	10	10
70	x	10	10	x	4	x	10	=	40	=	=	7
5	100	10	=	=	10	10	=	30	8	10	20	9
120	x	3	=	110	100	=	80	10	x	x	11	x
8	110	10	x	80	1	50	60	120	10	10	120	10
x	60	100	=	10	x	10	=	100	=	=	110	=
10	11	x	10	60	=	110	90	20	90	40	8	90
=	12	x	10	=	120	30	3	x	10	=	40	9
80	120	6	x	12	=	40	7	x	10	=	70	30

2

Set 1	Set 2	Set 3	Set 4	Set 5	Set 6	Set 7	Set 8	Set 9
1 x 10 = **10**	100 = **10** x 10	**9** x 10 = 90	50 = **5** x 10	1 = **10** ÷ 10	**120** ÷ 10 = 12	30 ÷ 10 = **3**	**11** = 110 ÷ 10	50 = **5** x 10
10 = 100 ÷ 10	4 x 10 = **40**	80 = **8** x 10	**60** = 6 x 10	**2** = 20 ÷ 10	4 = **40** ÷ 10	**40** ÷ 10 = 4	5 = **50** ÷ 10	**60** = 6 x 10
11 = 110 ÷ 10	5 x 10 = **50**	10 x 10 = **100**	11 x 10 = **110**	70 ÷ 10 = **7**	12 = **120** ÷ 10	6 = **60** ÷ 10	**6** = 60 ÷ 10	**11** x 10 = 110
6 x 10 = 60	**5** = 50 ÷ 10	**120** ÷ 10 = 12	**30** ÷ 10 = 3	**80** ÷ 10 = 8	60 ÷ 10 = **6**	110 = **11** x 10	110 = **11** x 10	30 ÷ 10 = **3**
7 x 10 = **70**	6 = **60** ÷ 10	4 = **40** ÷ 10	40 ÷ 10 = **4**	**90** = 9 x 10	100 ÷ 10 = **10**	120 = **12** x 10	120 = **12** x 10	**40** = 4 x 10
12 x 10 = **120**	**110** = 11 x 10	12 = **120** ÷ 10	**50** ÷ 10 = 5	2 x 10 = **20**	**90** = 9 x 10	**10** ÷ 10 = 1	**10** ÷ 10 = 1	5 = **50** ÷ 10
10 = 1 x 10	120 = **12** x 10	60 ÷ 10 = **6**	30 = **3** x 10	**3** x 10 = 30	**100** = 10 x 10	20 ÷ 10 = **2**	6 x 10 = **60**	**6** = 60 ÷ 10
20 = 2 x 10	**10** ÷ 10 = 1	**100** ÷ 10 = 10	70 = 7 x 10	7 = **70** ÷ 10	4 x 10 = **40**	**50** ÷ 10 = 5	7 x 10 = 70	110 = **11** x 10
3 = 30 ÷ 10	**20** ÷ 10 = 2	**110** ÷ 10 = 11	**1** = 10 ÷ 10	**8** = 80 ÷ 10	5 x 10 = 50	30 = **3** x 10	12 x 10 = **120**	50 ÷ 10 = **5**
90 = **9** x 10	8 x 10 = **80**	40 = **4** x 10	2 = **20** ÷ 10	9 = **90** ÷ 10	5 = **50** ÷ 10	70 = **7** x 10	10 = **1** x 10	30 = **3** x 10

3

1

10	40	60	90	45	43	68	96	24	20	87	46	40
34	42	46	30	100	35	75	36	97	35	88	53	25
43	20	120	70	34	78	97	110	24	66	86	120	75
24	35	65	110	67	33	24	120	77	90	57	35	35
65	30	78	120	10	80	60	30	65	40	80	54	98
23	54	10	46	30	64	77	90	43	57	86	99	64
78	23	34	110	36	46	54	10	60	90	50	65	36
90	85	65	35	74	76	45	20	46	64	34	35	87
90	50	33	85	24	100	30	40	43	30	5	88	40
87	36	100	57	86	22	53	60	47	7	67	97	54
54	96	35	7	60	34	65	30	40	80	70	20	Exit

2

a	10 + 10 + 10 + 10 + 10	5 x 10	50
b	**10 + 10 + 10 + 10 + 10 + 10 + 10 + 10 + 10 + 10 + 10 + 10**	**12 x 10**	120
c	10	**1 x 10**	10
d	10 + 10 + 10 + 10 + 10 + 10 + 10 + 10 + 10 + 10 + 10	11 x 10	**110**
e	**10 + 10 + 10 + 10 + 10 + 10**	**6 x 10**	60
f	10 + 10	**2 x 10**	**20**
g	**10 + 10 + 10 + 10 + 10 + 10 + 10 + 10 + 10 + 10**	10 x 10	**100**
h	10 + 10 + 10 + 10 + 10 + 10 + 10	**7 x 10**	70
i	**10 + 10 + 10 + 10 + 10 + 10 + 10 + 10**	**8 x 10**	80
j	10 + 10 + 10 + 10	**4 x 10**	**40**
k	10 + 10 + 10 + 10 + 10 + 10 + 10 + 10 + 10	**9 x 10**	**90**
l	**10 + 10 + 10**	**3 x 10**	30

4

1

a   70 cm^2
b   10 cm^2
c   90 cm^2
d   80 cm^2
e   100 cm^2
f   110 cm^2
g   50 cm^2
h   60 cm^2
i   30 cm^2
j   40 cm^2
k   120 cm^2

2

a   500 cm^2
b   1,200 cm^2
c   400 cm^2

5

1

a 20, 200, 2,000
b 30, 300, 3,000
c 40, 400, 4,000
d 50, 500, 5,000
e 60, 600, 6,000
f 70, 700, 7,000
g 80, 800, 8,000
h 90, 900, 9,000
i 100, 1,000, 10,000
j 110, 1,100, 11,000
k 120, 1,200, 12,000

2

a $3 \times 10 = 30$
b $90 \div 10 = 9$
c $10 \times 10 = 100$
d $5 \times 10 = 50$
e $10 \div 10 = 1$
f $120 \div 10 = 12$
g $40 \div 10 = 4$
h $6 \times 10 = 60$
i $7 \times 10 = 70$
j $110 \div 10 = 11$
k $2 \times 10 = 20$
l $80 \div 10 = 8$

6

1

2

a $120 \div 10$ (12) ▶ 3×10 (30) ▶ 4×10 (40) ▶ 11×10 (110) ▶ 100×10 (1,000)
b $30 \div 10$ (3) ▶ $50 \div 10$ (5) 2×10 (20) ▶ 11×10 (110) ▶ $1,200 \div 10$ (120)
c $50 \div 10$ (5) ▶ $110 \div 10$ (11) ▶ 3×10 (30) ▶ 60×10 (600) ▶ 90×10 (900)
d $80 \div 10$ (8) ▶ $300 \div 10$ (30) ▶ 12×10 (120) ▶ 60×10 (600) ▶ 500×10 (5,000)

7

1 $30 \div 10 = 3$
2 $5 \times 10 = 50$
3 $10 \div 10 = 1$
4 $12 \times 10 = 120$
5 $80 \div 10 = 8$
6 $110 \div 10 = 11$
7 $8 \times 10 = 80$
8 $90 \div 10 = 9$
9 $10 \times 4 = 40$
10 $15 \times 10 = 150$
11 $30 \times 10 = 300$
12 $120 \times 10 = 1,200$
13 $80 \times 10 = 800$
14 $450 \div 10 = 45$

8

1 $\frac{2}{3} = \frac{20}{\mathbf{30}}$

2 $\frac{70}{80} = \frac{\mathbf{7}}{8}$

3 $\frac{3}{5} = \frac{\mathbf{30}}{50}$

4 $\frac{\mathbf{110}}{120} = \frac{11}{12}$

5 $\frac{10}{\mathbf{11}} = \frac{100}{110}$

6 $\frac{\mathbf{40}}{50} = \frac{4}{5}$

7 $\frac{20}{80} = \frac{2}{\mathbf{8}}$

8 $\frac{\mathbf{4}}{12} = \frac{40}{120}$

9 $\frac{3}{11} = \frac{30}{\mathbf{110}}$

10 $\frac{10}{60} = \frac{\mathbf{1}}{6}$

11 $\frac{10}{40} = \frac{1}{\mathbf{4}}$

12 $\frac{1}{\mathbf{7}} = \frac{10}{70}$

13 $\frac{5}{11} = \frac{\mathbf{50}}{110}$

14 $\frac{50}{\mathbf{80}} = \frac{5}{8}$

15 $\frac{10}{50} = \frac{1}{\mathbf{5}}$

16 $\frac{\mathbf{3}}{11} = \frac{30}{110}$

17 $\frac{9}{12} = \frac{90}{\mathbf{120}}$

18 $\frac{4}{7} = \frac{40}{70}$

19 $\frac{8}{11} = \frac{80}{\mathbf{110}}$

20 $\frac{50}{60} = \frac{\mathbf{5}}{6}$

21 $\frac{100}{110} = \frac{10}{\mathbf{11}}$

22 $\frac{5}{9} = \frac{50}{90}$

9

1 70
2 40
3 30
4 110
5 100
6 120
7 90
8 60
9 20
10 50
11 250
12 200
13 500
14 130
15 150
16 600
17 300
18 400

10

1 7
2 2
3 10
4 3
5 8
6 6
7 11
8 9
9 1
10 12
11 4
12 80
13 100
14 120
15 30
16 110
17 77
18 70

11

1 2,000 ml milk, 30 bananas, 20 chocolate bars
2 2,000 g oats, 1,200 g butter, 1,100 g brown sugar
3 40 g sugar, 50 ml cream, 30 g butter
4 20 g flour, 7 g sugar, 20 g butter, 8 g dried fruit
5 110 strawberries, 90 cherries, 500 ml yoghurt, 1,000 ml juice

12

1 $10 \text{ cm} \times 10 = 100 \text{ cm}$
2 $12 \text{ cm} \ 10 = 120 \text{ cm}$
3 $4 \text{ cm} \times 10 = 40 \text{ cm}$
4 $11 \text{ cm} \times 10 = 110 \text{ cm}$
5 $8 \text{ cm} \times 10 = 80 \text{ cm}$
6 $9 \text{ cm} \times 10 = 90 \text{ cm}$
7 $10 \text{ cm} \times 5 = 50 \text{ cm}$
8 $10 \text{ cm} \times 4 = 40 \text{ cm}$
9 $10 \text{ cm} \times 3 = 30 \text{ cm}$
10 $100 \text{ cm} \times 6 = 600 \text{ cm}$
11 $100 \text{ cm} \times 7 = 700 \text{ cm}$
12 $100 \text{ cm} \times 9 = 900 \text{ cm}$

11 times table

1

1

1	2	3	4	5	6	7	8	9	10
11	12	13	14	15	16	17	18	19	20
21	**22**	23	24	25	26	27	28	29	30
31	32	**33**	34	35	36	37	38	39	40
41	42	43	**44**	45	46	47	48	49	50
51	52	53	54	**55**	56	57	58	59	60
61	62	63	64	65	**66**	67	68	69	70
71	72	73	74	75	76	**77**	78	79	80
81	82	83	84	85	86	87	**88**	89	90
91	92	93	94	95	96	97	98	**99**	100

2

1	x	11	=	11	4	22	110	3	8	1	x	11
9	88	10	x	11	=	5	132	121	7	x	77	88
99	11	8	12	10	x	11	x	55	x	11	11	121
110	11	x	77	x	132	4	77	11	11	=	66	=
4	x	11	2	33	11	110	33	10	=	22	77	3
4	11	=	4	x	11	=	44	x	77	55	121	x
x	=	77	8	110	11	66	132	11	3	8	9	11
11	121	88	55	x	x	=	121	=	x	x	x	=
=	132	5	x	11	11	x	22	110	11	11	11	33
66	2	x	11	=	33	=	11	44	=	=	=	11
3	6	x	11	=	66	22	88	132	44	99	99	88

2

Set 1	Set 2	Set 3	Set 4	Set 5	Set 6	Set 7	Set 8	Set 9
132 ÷ 11 = **12**	**66** ÷ 11 = 6	11 x 11 = **121**	**7** = 77 ÷ 11	**99** = 9 x 11	**88** ÷ 11 = 8	66 = **6** x 11	**7** x 11 = 77	2 = **22** ÷ 11
1 = **11** ÷ 11	8 x 11 = **88**	**77** = 7 x 11	8 = **88** ÷ 11	110 = **10** x 11	99 ÷ 11 = **9**	**7** = 77 ÷ 11	5 x 11 = **55**	**3** = 33 ÷ 11
2 = 22 ÷ 11	**33** ÷ 11 = 3	88 = **8** x 11	**9** = 99 ÷ 11	**121** = 11 x 11	110 ÷ 11 = **10**	8 = **88** ÷ 11	77 = **7** x 11	4 = **44** ÷ 11
3 = **33** ÷ 11	5 = **55** ÷ 11	**77** ÷ 11 = 7	10 = **110** ÷ 11	132 = **12** x 11	**121** ÷ 11 = 11	**9** = 99 ÷ 11	88 = 8 x 11	**6** x 11 = 66
4 = **44** ÷ 11	6 = **66** ÷ 11	88 ÷ 11 = **8**	11 = **121** ÷ 11	11 ÷ 11 = **1**	55 = **5** x 11	10 = **110** ÷ 11	77 ÷ 11 = **7**	**55** ÷ 11 = 5
6 x 11 = 66	3 x 11 = **33**	**99** ÷ 11 = 9	**12** = 132 ÷ 11	**11** = 1 x 11	6 = 66 ÷ 11	11 = **121** ÷ 11	88 ÷ 11 = **8**	66 ÷ 11 = **6**
7 x 11 = **77**	**4** x 11 = 44	110 ÷ 11 = **10**	12 x 11 = **132**	2 x 11 = **22**	3 x 11 = **33**	**12** = 132 ÷ 11	**99** ÷ 11 = 9	8 x 11 = **88**
5 x 11 = **55**	**44** = 4 x 11	**121** ÷ 11 = 11	33 = **3** x 11	9 x 11 = 99	**4** x 11 = 44	12 x 11 = **132**	**44** ÷ 11 = 4	33 ÷ 11 = **3**
44 ÷ 11 = 4	1 x 11 = **11**	**55** = 5 x 11	**99** = 9 x 11	11 = **1** x 11	44 = **4** x 11	**33** = 3 x 11	55 ÷ 11 = **5**	5 = **55** ÷ 11
55 ÷ 11 = **5**	**10** x 11 = 110	66 = **6** x 11	110 = **10** x 11	22 = **2** x 11	1 x 11 = **11**	99 = **9** x 11	**66** ÷ 11 = 6	**7** x 11 = 77

3

1

66	34	34	132	33	56	32	77	22	75	24	64	121
22	32	66	34	45	32	77	32	75	121	99	65	132
55	25	89	64	77	66	78	43	35	77	15	110	46
33	88	76	46	88	6	46	45	56	54	76	132	86
77	99	22	110	121	132	11	22	45	75	43	121	34
56	11	46	88	75	92	34	55	77	99	88	66	24
23	22	86	35	76	37	85	34	33	32	24	44	74
32	77	57	74	22	66	44	24	55	45	44	55	77
77	35	43	7	34	33	86	46	36	75	35	33	43
56	32	65	66	75	35	77	22	66	25	86	121	46
63	45	23	88	110	43	67	43	78	32	54	132	Exit

2

a	11 + 11 + 11 + 11 + 11 + 11 + 11	7 x 11	77
b	**11 + 11 + 11**	**3 x 11**	33
c	11 + 11 + 11 + 11 + 11 + 11 + 11 + 11	**8 x 11**	**88**
d	11 + 11 + 11 + 11 + 11	**5 x 11**	55
e	**11 + 11 + 11 + 11 + 11 + 11 + 11 + 11 + 11 + 11**	10 x 11	**110**
f	11 + 11	**2 x 11**	22
g	**11 + 11 + 11 + 11 + 11 + 11 + 11 + 11 + 11 + 11 + 11 + 11**	**12 x 11**	132
h	**11 + 11 + 11 + 11 + 11 + 11 + 11 + 11 + 11**	9 x 11	**99**
i	11 + 11 + 11 + 11 + 11 + 11 + 11 + 11 + 11 + 11 + 11	**11 x 11**	121
j	11	**1 x 11**	11
k	11 + 11 + 11 + 11 + 11 + 11	**6 x 11**	**66**
l	**11 + 11 + 11 + 11**	**4 x 11**	44

4

1

a 99 cm²
b 11 cm²
c 121 cm²
d 110 cm²
e 132 cm²
f 55 cm²
g 33 cm²
h 44 cm²
i 66 cm²
j 88 cm²
k 77 cm²

2

a 550 cm²
b 1,320 cm²
c 440 cm²

ANSWERS

5

1

a 22, 220, 2,200
b 33, 330, 3,300
c 44, 440, 4,400
d 55, 550, 5,500
e 66, 660, 6,600
f 77, 770, 7,700
g 88, 880, 8,800
h 99, 990, 9,900
i 110, 1,100, 11,000
j 121, 1,210, 12,100
k 132, 1,320, 13,200

2

a 308
b 825
c 429
d 627
e 528
f 3,124
g 5,192
h 4,345

6

1 69
2 85
3 79
4 121
5 152
6 253
7 225
8 214
9 362
10 142
11 356
12 215
13 654
14 252
15 245
16 365
17 286

7

1 $132 \div 11 = 12$
2 $5 \times 11 = 55$
3 $77 \div 11 = 7$
4 $121 \div 11 = 11$
5 $8 \times 11 = 88$
6 $11 \div 11 = 1$
7 $6 \times 11 = 66$
8 $110 \div 11 = 10$
9 $11 \times 11 = 121$
10 $40 \times 11 = 440$
11 $660 \text{ g} \div 11 \text{ g} = 60$
12 $30 \times 11 = 330$
13 $£80 \times 11 = £880$
14 $1,210 \div 11 = 110$

8

1 $\dfrac{2}{3} = \dfrac{22}{\mathbf{33}}$

2 $\dfrac{77}{88} = \dfrac{7}{\mathbf{8}}$

3 $\dfrac{3}{5} = \dfrac{\mathbf{33}}{55}$

4 $\dfrac{121}{132} = \dfrac{11}{\mathbf{12}}$

5 $\dfrac{\mathbf{110}}{121} = \dfrac{10}{11}$

6 $\dfrac{44}{55} = \dfrac{4}{\mathbf{5}}$

7 $\dfrac{22}{88} = \dfrac{\mathbf{2}}{8}$

8 $\dfrac{4}{\mathbf{12}} = \dfrac{44}{132}$

9 $\dfrac{3}{11} = \dfrac{\mathbf{33}}{121}$

10 $\dfrac{11}{\mathbf{66}} = \dfrac{1}{6}$

11 $\dfrac{11}{44} = \dfrac{\mathbf{1}}{4}$

12 $\dfrac{1}{7} = \dfrac{11}{\mathbf{77}}$

13 $\dfrac{5}{11} = \dfrac{\mathbf{55}}{121}$

14 $\dfrac{\mathbf{55}}{88} = \dfrac{5}{8}$

15 $\dfrac{11}{55} = \dfrac{1}{\mathbf{5}}$

16 $\dfrac{\mathbf{3}}{11} = \dfrac{33}{121}$

17 $\dfrac{9}{12} = \dfrac{99}{\mathbf{132}}$

18 $\dfrac{\mathbf{4}}{7} = \dfrac{44}{77}$

19 $\dfrac{8}{11} = \dfrac{\mathbf{88}}{121}$

20 $\dfrac{55}{66} = \dfrac{\mathbf{5}}{6}$

21 $\dfrac{110}{121} = \dfrac{10}{\mathbf{11}}$

22 $\dfrac{\mathbf{5}}{9} = \dfrac{55}{99}$

9

1 77
2 44
3 33
4 121
5 110
6 132
7 99
8 66
9 22
10 55
11 275
12 220
13 550
14 770
15 330
16 1,210
17 660
18 11,000

10

1 3
2 9
3 4
4 7
5 11
6 5
7 10
8 12
9 8
10 1
11 2
12 13
13 15
14 20
15 25
16 30
17 100
18 50

11

1 3,300 ml milk, 33 bananas, 22 chocolate bars
2 2,200 g oats, 1,320 g butter, 1,210 g brown sugar
3 40 g sugar, 50 ml cream, 30 g butter
4 20 g flour, 7 g sugar, 20 g butter, 10 g dried fruit
5 121 strawberries, 99 cherries, 550 ml yoghurt, 1,100 ml juice

12

1 $10 \text{ cm} \times 11 = 110 \text{ cm}$
2 $12 \text{ cm} \times 11 = 132 \text{ cm}$
3 $4 \text{ cm} \times 11 = 44 \text{ cm}$
4 $11 \text{ cm} \times 11 = 121 \text{ cm}$
5 $8 \text{ cm} \times 11 = 88 \text{ cm}$
6 $9 \text{ cm} \times 11 = 99 \text{ cm}$
7 $11 \text{ cm} \times 5 = 55 \text{ cm}$
8 $11 \text{ cm} \times 6 = 66 \text{ cm}$
9 $11 \text{ cm} \times 7 = 77 \text{ cm}$
10 $110 \text{ cm} \times 9 = 990 \text{ cm}$
11 $110 \text{ cm} \times 4 = 440 \text{ cm}$
12 $110 \text{ cm} \times 3 = 330 \text{ cm}$

12 times table

1

1

1	2	3	4	5	6	7	8	9	10
11	12	13	14	15	16	17	18	19	20
21	22	23	24	25	26	27	28	29	30
31	32	33	34	35	36	37	38	39	40
41	42	43	44	45	46	47	48	49	50
51	52	53	54	55	56	57	58	59	60
61	62	63	64	65	66	67	68	69	70
71	72	73	74	75	76	77	78	79	80
81	82	83	84	85	86	87	88	89	90
91	92	93	94	95	96	97	98	99	100

2

1	x	12	=	12	6	10	4	x	12	=	60	5
12	10	x	12	=	x	x	4	96	48	6	84	x
4	108	12	3	2	12	12	144	x	120	x	132	12
3	120	=	9	x	=	=	2	1	12	12	84	=
5	x	144	x	12	12	120	8	x	72	=	36	72
11	36	12	12	=	144	=	12	x	12	72	48	8
x	144	60	=	24	8	7	36	132	12	=	144	x
12	96	132	120	24	9	x	12	=	108	=	48	12
=	7	x	12	=	84	11	x	12	=	84	70	=
132	12	x	12	=	7	x	12	=	72	132	120	96
1	x	12	=	36	84	5	x	12	=	60	24	120

2

Set 1	Set 2	Set 3	Set 4	Set 5	Set 6	Set 7	Set 8	Set 9
7 x 12 = **84**	**120** ÷ 12 = 10	1 = **12** ÷ 12	5 x 12 = **60**	8 = **96** ÷ 12	144 = **12** x 12	12 = **1** x 12	**132** = 11 x 12	**120** ÷ 12 = 10
8 x 12 = 96	36 = **3** x 12	11 x 12 = **132**	**6** x 12 = 72	**9** = 108 ÷ 12	**12** ÷ 12 = 1	**60** = 5 x 12	12 = **144** ÷ 12	3 x 12 = **36**
9 x 12 = **108**	**48** = 4 x 12	**108** ÷ 12 = 9	**108** = 9 x 12	10 = **120** ÷ 12	**84** = 7 x 12	72 = **6** x 12	1 x 12 = **12**	4 x 12 = 48
11 = **132** ÷ 12	**10** x 12 = 120	2 = **24** ÷ 12	**120** = 10 x 12	108 = **9** x 12	96 = **8** x 12	**24** = 2 x 12	**2** x 12 = 24	**24** = 2 x 12
12 = 144 ÷ 12	48 ÷ 12 = **4**	3 = **36** ÷ 12	132 = **11** x 12	**120** = 10 x 12	24 ÷ 12 = **2**	**36** = 3 x 12	120 = **10** x 12	**36** = 3 x 12
1 x 12 = 12	60 ÷ 12 = **5**	**12** = 1 x 12	**144** = 12 x 12	132 = **11** x 12	**36** ÷ 12 = 3	48 = **4** x 12	**144** = 12 x 12	48 = **4** x 12
2 x 12 = **24**	**72** ÷ 12 = 6	60 = **5** x 12	**12** ÷ 12 = 1	60 ÷ 12 = **5**	96 ÷ 12 = **8**	10 x 12 = **120**	12 ÷ 12 = **1**	**48** ÷ 12 = 4
3 x 12 = **36**	84 ÷ 12 = **7**	**72** = 6 x 12	84 = **7** x 12	**72** ÷ 12 = 6	5 = **60** ÷ 12	120 ÷ 12 = **10**	84 = **7** x 12	60 ÷ 12 = **5**
4 x 12 = 48	**132** ÷ 12 = 11	4 = **48** ÷ 12	96 = **8** x 12	84 ÷ 12 = **7**	6 = **72** ÷ 12	4 = **48** ÷ 12	**3** x 12 = 36	72 ÷ 12 = **6**
24 = **2** x 12	**144** ÷ 12 = 12	12 x 12 = **144**	**24** ÷ 12 = 2	**132** ÷ 12 = 11	**7** = 84 ÷ 12	12 x 12 = **144**	4 x 12 = **48**	**84** ÷ 12 = 7

3

1

12	34	44	26	86	96	22	75	60	72	84	96	56
72	6	24	43	56	77	12	24	36	86	43	108	43
96	43	56	65	34	65	72	54	24	54	87	120	67
108	144	96	36	48	120	132	24	31	65	24	132	33
67	86	84	46	96	14	12	57	72	22	54	144	24
44	35	108	66	84	132	43	53	24	35	46	60	65
31	87	120	45	46	14	75	45	48	54	65	72	32
146	44	4	6	43	144	23	36	72	84	120	96	54
44	67	75	4	120	75	43	60	22	32	27	48	19
24	24	6	34	144	35	36	132	44	42	63	58	73
76	124	54	44	32	12	64	144	12	36	24	96	exit

2

a	12 + 12 + 12 + 12 + 12	5 x 12	60
b	**12 + 12 + 12 + 12 + 12 + 12 + 12 + 12**	**8 x 12**	96
c	12 + 12 + 12 + 12 + 12 + 12	**6 x 12**	72
d	12	**1 x 12**	**12**
e	**12 + 12 + 12 + 12 + 12 + 12 + 12 + 12 + 12 + 12 + 12 + 12**	12 x 12	**144**
f	12 + 12 + 12 + 12 + 12 + 12 + 12 + 12 + 12	**9 x 12**	108
g	**12 + 12 + 12 + 12 + 12 + 12 + 12 + 12 + 12 + 12 + 12**	**11 x 12**	132
h	12 + 12 + 12	**3 x 12**	**36**
i	12 + 12 + 12 + 12 + 12 + 12 + 12	**7 x 12**	84
j	**12 + 12**	**2 x 12**	24
k	12 + 12 + 12 + 12 + 12 + 12 + 12 + 12 + 12 + 12	**10 x 12**	**120**
l	**12 + 12 + 12 + 12**	4 x 12	**48**

4

1

a 120 cm^2
b 12 cm^2
c 132 cm^2
d 108 cm^2
e 60 cm^2
f 48 cm^2
g 36 cm^2
h 72 cm^2
i 84 cm^2
j 96 cm^2
k 144 cm^2

2

a 600 cm^2
b 1,440 cm^2
c 4,800 cm^2

ANSWERS

5

1

a   24, 240, 2,400
b   36, 360, 3,600
c   48, 480, 4,800
d   60, 600, 6,000
e   72, 720, 7,200
f   84, 840, 8,400
g   96, 960, 9,600
h   108, 1,080, 10,800
i   120, 1,200, 12,000
j   132, 1,320, 13,200
k   144, 1,440, 14,400

2

a   336
b   900
c   468
d   684
e   576
f   3,408
g   5,664
h   4,740

6

1   69
2   59
3   145
4   127
5   114
6   165
7   118
8   228
9   186
10   153
11   268
12   175
13   578
14   475
15   258
16   169
17   247

7

1   $8 \times 12 = 96$
2   $108 \div 12 = 9$
3   $7 \times 12 = 84$
4   $36 \div 12 = 3$
5   $6 \times 12 = 72$
6   $£2 \times 12 = £24$
7   $4 \times 12 = 48$
8   $3 \times 12 = 36$
9   $5 \times 12 = 60$
10   $180 \div 12 = 15$
11   $360 \div 12 = 30$
12   $20 \times 12 = 240$
13   $£960 \div £12 = 80$
14   $30 \times 12 = 360$

8

1   $\dfrac{2}{3} = \dfrac{24}{\mathbf{36}}$

2   $\dfrac{84}{96} = \dfrac{\mathbf{7}}{8}$

3   $\dfrac{3}{5} = \dfrac{36}{\mathbf{60}}$

4   $\dfrac{132}{144} = \dfrac{\mathbf{11}}{12}$

5   $\dfrac{120}{132} = \dfrac{\mathbf{10}}{11}$

6   $\dfrac{48}{\mathbf{60}} = \dfrac{4}{5}$

7   $\dfrac{24}{96} = \dfrac{\mathbf{2}}{8}$

8   $\dfrac{4}{12} = \dfrac{48}{\mathbf{144}}$

9   $\dfrac{3}{11} = \dfrac{\mathbf{36}}{132}$

10   $\dfrac{12}{\mathbf{72}} = \dfrac{1}{6}$

11   $\dfrac{12}{48} = \dfrac{\mathbf{1}}{4}$

12   $\dfrac{1}{7} = \dfrac{12}{\mathbf{84}}$

13   $\dfrac{\mathbf{5}}{11} = \dfrac{60}{132}$

14   $\dfrac{60}{96} = \dfrac{5}{\mathbf{8}}$

15   $\dfrac{12}{60} = \dfrac{1}{\mathbf{5}}$

16   $\dfrac{\mathbf{3}}{11} = \dfrac{36}{132}$

17   $\dfrac{9}{\mathbf{12}} = \dfrac{108}{144}$

18   $\dfrac{4}{7} = \dfrac{48}{\mathbf{84}}$

19   $\dfrac{8}{11} = \dfrac{\mathbf{96}}{132}$

20   $\dfrac{60}{72} = \dfrac{5}{\mathbf{6}}$

21   $\dfrac{120}{132} = \dfrac{\mathbf{10}}{11}$

22   $\dfrac{5}{9} = \dfrac{60}{\mathbf{108}}$

9

1   84
2   48
3   36
4   132
5   120
6   144
7   108
8   72
9   24
10   60
11   300
12   240
13   600
14   840
15   480
16   360
17   960
18   1,080

10

1   10
2   4
3   7
4   12
5   1
6   2
7   8
8   5
9   9
10   11
11   3
12   30
13   40
14   70
15   90
16   120
17   50
18   20

11

1   3,600 ml milk, 36 bananas, 24 chocolate bars
2   2,400 g oats, 1,440 g butter, 1,320 g brown sugar
3   40 g sugar, 50 ml cream, 30 g butter
4   20 g flour, 10 g sugar, 30 g butter, 6 g dried fruit
5   132 strawberries, 108 cherries, 600 ml yoghurt, 1,200 ml juice

12

1   $10 \text{ cm} \times 12 = 120 \text{ cm}$
2   $12 \text{ cm} \times 12 = 144 \text{ cm}$
3   $4 \text{ cm} \times 12 = 48 \text{ cm}$
4   $11 \text{ cm} \times 12 = 132 \text{ cm}$
5   $8 \text{ cm} \times 12 = 96 \text{ cm}$
6   $9 \text{ cm} \times 12 = 108 \text{ cm}$
7   $12 \text{ cm} \times 5 = 60 \text{ cm}$
8   $12 \text{ cm} \times 6 = 72 \text{ cm}$
9   $12 \text{ cm} \times 7 = 84 \text{ cm}$
10   $120 \text{ cm} \times 4 = 480 \text{ cm}$
11   $120 \text{ cm} \times 3 = 360 \text{ cm}$
12   $120 \text{ cm} \times 9 = 1,080 \text{ cm}$

Mixed tables

1

Set 1	Set 2	Set 3	Set 4	Set 5	Set 6	Set 7	Set 8	Set 9
1 x 9 = 9	**2** ÷ 2 = 1	90 = 10 x **9**	27 ÷ 9 = **3**	**11** = 99 ÷ 9	2 x **2** = 4	**5** = 10 ÷ 2	99 ÷ 11 = **9**	72 ÷ 9 = **8**
11 x **4** = 44	6 = 18 ÷ **3**	**72** = 8 x 9	22 ÷ **2** = 11	8 x 3 = **24**	6 x 4 = **24**	5 x **4** = 20	3 x **4** = 12	**20** = 4 x 5
54 = 9 x **6**	**8** x 5 = 40	84 = 7 x **12**	3 x 6 = **18**	4 = **24** ÷ 6	40 = **8** x 5	77 = **7** x 11	**18** = 3 x 6	24 ÷ **6** = 4
5 = 35 ÷ 7	54 = **9** x 6	**88** = 11 x 8	**27** = 3 x 9	11 x 10 = **110**	12 x 5 = **60**	7 x 7 = **49**	24 = 4 x **6**	8 x 8 = **64**
8 x **7** = 56	3 x 10 = **30**	11 x 12 = **132**	5 x 4 = **20**	30 ÷ **10** = 3	132 = **11** x 12	11 x **5** = 55	**24** = 2 x 12	**60** ÷ 10 = 6
72 = **12** x 6	6 = **54** ÷ 9	**108** ÷ 12 = 9	**9** = 81 ÷ 9	8 x 6 = **48**	60 ÷ **12** = 5	5 x 6 = **30**	32 ÷ **8** = 4	100 ÷ **10** = 10
9 = 72 ÷ **8**	**4** x 12 = 48	96 = **12** x 8	16 = 4 x **4**	**144** = 12 x 12	12 = 72 ÷ **6**	**6** = 30 ÷ 5	56 ÷ 8 = **7**	8 = 72 ÷ **9**
28 = 7 x 4	50 = 10 x **5**	4 x 6 = **24**	**11** x 8 = 88	**36** = 12 x 3	60 ÷ 10 = **6**	16 = **4** x 4	**12** x 5 = 60	**21** = 7 x 3
8 x **2** = 16	**12** ÷ 4 = 3	**21** = 7 x 3	4 x 8 = **32**	49 = **7** x 7	20 = **5** x 4	**27** ÷ 3 = 9	32 ÷ **4** = 8	24 = **12** x 2
99 ÷ 9 = **11**	10 ÷ 2 = **5**	6 ÷ 3 = **2**	24 ÷ 2 = **12**	12 = 108 ÷ **9**	12 = 36 ÷ **3**	8 x 9 = **72**	21 ÷ 3 = **7**	5 x 2 = **10**

2

1 $\dfrac{2}{5} = \dfrac{14}{\mathbf{35}}$

2 $\dfrac{42}{54} = \dfrac{\mathbf{7}}{9}$

3 $\dfrac{2}{7} = \dfrac{18}{\mathbf{63}}$

4 $\dfrac{\mathbf{99}}{108} = \dfrac{11}{12}$

5 $\dfrac{4}{16} = \dfrac{2}{\mathbf{8}}$

6 $\dfrac{18}{21} = \dfrac{\mathbf{6}}{7}$

7 $\dfrac{\mathbf{33}}{121} = \dfrac{3}{11}$

8 $\dfrac{4}{\mathbf{9}} = \dfrac{32}{72}$

9 $\dfrac{3}{11} = \dfrac{15}{\mathbf{55}}$

10 $\dfrac{\mathbf{12}}{96} = \dfrac{1}{8}$

11 $\dfrac{\mathbf{24}}{66} = \dfrac{4}{11}$

12 $\dfrac{1}{6} = \dfrac{3}{\mathbf{18}}$

13 $\dfrac{2}{11} = \dfrac{4}{\mathbf{22}}$

14 $\dfrac{70}{80} = \dfrac{\mathbf{7}}{8}$

15 $\dfrac{9}{45} = \dfrac{1}{\mathbf{5}}$

16 $\dfrac{6}{11} = \dfrac{\mathbf{54}}{99}$

17 $\dfrac{11}{12} = \dfrac{44}{\mathbf{48}}$

18 $\dfrac{4}{7} = \dfrac{\mathbf{32}}{56}$

19 $\dfrac{\mathbf{8}}{11} = \dfrac{32}{44}$

20 $\dfrac{\mathbf{35}}{42} = \dfrac{5}{6}$

21 $\dfrac{110}{121} = \dfrac{10}{\mathbf{11}}$

22 $\dfrac{5}{9} = \dfrac{\mathbf{40}}{72}$

3

1

a 80 cm²
b 32 cm²
c 14 cm²
d 44 cm²
e 49 cm²
f 84 cm²
g 10 cm²
h 27 cm²
i 36 cm²
j 96 cm²
k 24 cm²
l 72 cm²
m 56 cm²

2

a 2,400 cm²
b 3,300 cm²
c 1,800 cm²

4

1 32 ÷ 4 = 8
2 12 x 2 = 24
3 132 ÷ 12 = 11
4 7 x 8 = 56
5 8 x 3 = 24
6 9 x 5 = 45
7 18 ÷ 3 = 6
8 3 x 12 = 36
9 110 ÷ 11 = 10
10 90 x 2 = 180
11 80 ÷ 2 = 40
12 30 x 11 = 330
13 80 x 6 = 480
14 1,440 ÷ 30 = 48

5

1 2 hot chocolates: 400 ml milk, 60 g chocolate, 4 teaspoons cocoa.
5 hot chocolates: 1,000 ml milk, 150 g chocolate, 10 teaspoons cocoa.
11 hot chocolates: 2,200 ml milk, 330 g chocolate, 22 teaspoons cocoa.
2 3 smoothies: 300 ml milk, 180 ml yoghurt, 21 strawberries, 36 blackcurrants.
12 smoothies: 1,200 ml milk, 720 ml yoghurt, 84 strawberries, 144 blackcurrants.
6 smoothies: 600 ml milk, 360 ml yoghurt, 42 strawberries, 72 blackcurrants.
3 40 biscuits: 400 g butter, 200 g sugar, 480 g flour, 8 teaspoons cocoa.
70 biscuits: 700 g butter, 350 g sugar, 840 g flour, 14 teaspoons cocoa.
90 biscuits: 900 g butter, 450 g sugar, 1,080 g flour, 18 teaspoons cocoa.
4 80 Yorkshire puddings: 960 g flour, 32 eggs, 1,600 ml milk, 16 teaspoons oil.
60 Yorkshire puddings: 720 g flour, 24 eggs, 1,200 ml milk, 12 teaspoons oil.
90 Yorkshire puddings: 1,080 g flour, 36 eggs, 1,800 ml milk, 18 teaspoons oil.

ANSWERS

6

1 63
2 36
3 8
4 35
5 72
6 21
7 28
8 12
9 77
10 18
11 12
12 66
13 8
14 48
15 21
16 16
17 20
18 35

7

1 235
2 86
3 79
4 77
5 145
6 68
7 498
8 78
9 255
10 213
11 249
12 256
13 298
14 124
15 96
16 114
17 598

8

1 10 cm x 4 = 40 cm
2 12 cm x 5 = 60 cm
3 3 cm x 7 = 21 cm
4 6 cm x 10 = 60 cm
5 8 cm x 6 = 48 cm
6 6 cm x 9 = 54 cm
7 11 cm x 5 = 55 cm
8 4 cm x 12 = 48 cm
9 8 cm x 3 = 24cm
10 8 cm x 8 = 64 cm
11 5 cm x 4 = 20 cm
12 3 cm x 5 = 15 cm

9

1 600 x 4 = 2,400
2 7 x 60 = 420
3 40 x 90 = 3,600
4 4,000 ÷ 8 = 500
5 80 x 70 = 5,600
6 120 x 6 = 720
7 900 x 7 = 6,300
8 9 x 600 = 5,400
9 180 ÷ 6 = 30
10 4,400 ÷ 11 = 400
11 800 x 60 = 48,000
12 700 x 2 = 1,400
13 5 x 70 = 350
14 240 ÷ 8 = 30
15 700 x 9 = 6,300
16 8,000 x 3 = 24,000
17 60 x 50 = 3,000
18 900 x 5 = 4,500
19 4 x 800 = 3,200
20 900 ÷ 3 = 300
21 1,200 x 7 = 8,400
22 500 x 800 = 400,000
23 5,600 ÷ 8 = 700
24 600 x 90 = 54,000
25 500 x 7 = 3,500
26 3,200 ÷ 8 = 400
27 80 x 30 = 2,400
28 12 x 80 = 960
29 900 x 8 = 7,200
30 540 ÷ 9 = 60

10

1 64
2 45
3 40
4 42
5 99
6 90
7 132
8 24
9 120
10 21
11 40
12 121
13 72
14 90
15 72
16 42
17 88
18 72

11

1 7,886
2 2,732
3 1,746
4 1,715
5 1,635
6 5,067
7 6,024
8 4,584
9 2,372
10 4,865
11 5,176
12 4,068

12

1 3 cm x 4 cm = 12 cm^2
   12 cm^2 ÷ 2 = 6 cm^2
2 8 cm x 3 cm = 24 cm^2
   24 cm^2 ÷ 2 = 12 cm^2
3 4 cm x 7 cm = 28 cm^2
   28 cm^2 ÷ 2 = 14 cm^2
4 6 cm x 4 cm = 24 cm^2
   24 cm^2 ÷ 2 = 12 cm^2
5 10 cm x 6 cm = 60 cm^2
   60 cm^2 ÷ 2 = 30 cm^2
6 8 cm x 5 cm = 40 cm^2
   40 cm^2 ÷ 2 = 20 cm^2
7 11 cm x 4 cm = 44 cm^2
   44 cm^2 ÷ 2 = 22 cm^2
8 4 cm x 12 cm = 48 cm^2
   48 cm^2 ÷ 2 = 24 cm^2
9 6 cm x 3 cm = 18 cm^2
   18 cm^2 ÷ 2 = 9 cm^2
10 3 cm x 10 cm = 30 cm^2
    30 cm^2 ÷ 2 = 15 cm^2
11 4 cm x 4 cm = 16 cm^2
    16 cm^2 ÷ 2 = 8 cm^2
12 6 cm x 5 cm = 30 cm^2
    30 cm^2 ÷ 2 = 15 cm^2